UNIT 3 RESOURCE BOOK

Ancient and Classical Greece

McDougal Littell

World HISTORY

McDougal Littell
A DIVISION OF HOUGHTON MIFFLIN COMPANY

Evanston, Illinois • Boston • Dallas

ISBN-10: 0-547-01582-8 ISBN-13: 978-0-547-01582-8

1031405

1 2 3 4 5 6 7 8 9 - HWI - 12 11 10 09 08

Contents

Unit 3: Ancient and Classical Greece

Chapter 7: Ancient Greece

Starting with a Story 1

Reading Study Guide 3

Reading Study Guide 5

Reading Study Guide 7

Reading Study Guide 9

Reading Study Guide with Additional Support 11

Reading Study Guide with Additional Support 13

Reading Study Guide with Additional Support 15

Reading Study Guide with Additional Support 17

Guía de estudio de lectura 19

Guía de estudio de lectura 21

Guía de estudio de lectura 23

Guía de estudio de lectura 25

Guía de estudio de lectura con apoyo adicional 27

Guía de estudio de lectura con apoyo adicional 29

Guía de estudio de lectura con apoyo adicional 31

Guía de estudio de lectura con apoyo adicional 33

Building Background Vocabulary 35

Vocabulary Practice 36

Skillbuilder Practice 37

History Makers 39

Connect Geography & History 41

Outline Map Activity 43

Primary and Secondary Sources 45

Literature 46

Reader's Theater 47

Interdisciplinary Project 51

Interdisciplinary Project 52

Interdisciplinary Project 53

Interdisciplinary Project 54

Team Teaching Strategies 55

Bringing Social Studies Alive 57

Bringing Social Studies Alive 58

Bringing Social Studies Alive 59

Bringing Social Studies Alive 60

Bringing Social Studies Alive 61

Section 1 Quiz...65

Section 2 Quiz...66

Section 3 Quiz...67

Section 4 Quiz...68

Reteaching Activity..69

Reteaching Activity..70

Reteaching Activity..71

Reteaching Activity..72

Chapter Test A..73

Chapter Test B..79

Chapter Test C..85

Chapter 8: Classical Greece

Starting with a Story..91

Reading Study Guide...93

Reading Study Guide...95

Reading Study Guide...97

Reading Study Guide with Additional Support..........................99

Reading Study Guide with Additional Support.........................101

Reading Study Guide with Additional Support.........................103

Guía de estudio de lectura..105

Guía de estudio de lectura..107

Guía de estudio de lectura..109

Guía de estudio de lectura con apoyo adicional.......................111

Guía de estudio de lectura con apoyo adicional.......................113

Guía de estudio de lectura con apoyo adicional.......................115

Building Background Vocabulary..117

Vocabulary Practice...118

Skillbuilder Practice..119

History Makers...121

Connect Geography & History...123

Outline Map Activity..125

Outline Map Activity..127

Primary and Secondary Sources...129

Literature..130

Interdisciplinary Project..131

Interdisciplinary Project..132

Interdisciplinary Project..133

Interdisciplinary Project..134

Team Teaching Strategies..135

Bringing Social Studies Alive..137

Bringing Social Studies Alive 138

Bringing Social Studies Alive 139

Bringing Social Studies Alive 140

Bringing Social Studies Alive 141

Section 1 Quiz 143

Section 2 Quiz 144

Section 3 Quiz 145

Reteaching Activity 146

Reteaching Activity 147

Reteaching Activity 148

Chapter Test A 149

Chapter Test B 153

Chapter Test C 157

Writing About History 161

Answer Key 163

THE PERSIAN INVASION

Background: Ancient Greece was not a unified country. It was made up of independent city-states (states made of a city and its surrounding lands). Two of the leading city-states were Athens and Sparta. In 490 B.C., the mighty Persian Empire dominated Southwest Asia. The Persian king Darius decided to conquer Greece.

Darius and his army have just landed near Athens. Imagine that you are hearing the news in your home state of Sparta. Athens is 150 miles away. You wonder whether this fight has anything to do with you.

Source: Illustration by Frank Ordaz Studio

You are a soldier in Sparta. All of the free men in Sparta are soldiers. Your father and grandfather were soldiers. All of the men in your family for more than 150 years have been soldiers.

Sparta's army is its great strength and the source of its pride. From the time you were a boy, you trained to be a soldier. You learned to be tough. You and your friends played at war, preparing for the real thing.

Athens is Sparta's main rival. Its way of life is different. Men there spend most of their time talking about politics. Boys in Athens study debate, music, and poetry. You wonder what kind of people would waste their time on such things.

CHAPTER 7

An Athenian messenger has just arrived to tell the Spartan rulers that the Persian army has landed near Athens. He ran for two days to bring the news. He pleads with the rulers, "The enemy's force is enormous. There are 600 ships and more than 15,000 soldiers, many of them with horses. We have only about 10,000 soldiers. Athens desperately needs the help of your powerful army. Will you not join us in this fight?"

You've heard about the Persian Empire. Their rulers have been conquering their neighbors for more than 100 years. Their lands stretch from the Mediterranean Sea to the border of India. Persians now rule over Egypt.

Such a powerful empire might eliminate your rival for you. Then Sparta would be the greatest city-state in Greece. Why should Spartans die for men who would rather be politicians than warriors? Then a horrible thought occurs to you. What if the Persians don't stop with Athens? What if they decide to come after Sparta next?

Do you help your rival against a greater enemy?

Reading & Writing

1. **READING: Compare and Contrast** How were Athens and Sparta similar and different? Compare and contrast them.

2. **WRITING: Persuasion** Suppose that the rulers of Sparta have asked your advice. Think about the reasons for and against helping Athens. Then write a letter to the ruler explaining what you think Sparta should do.

SECTION

1 | READING STUDY GUIDE
The Geography of Greece

- **Before, You Learned** The geography of China influenced the ancient cultures that developed there.

- **Now You Will Learn** The geography of Greece led to sea travel and trade, which helped to influence Greek culture.

AS YOU READ Take notes listing the causes and effects in the section. Use the following causes/effects graphic organizers.

Causes	Effects
Mountains cover most of Greece.	The Greeks had difficulty . . . 1. 2.
Greece is nearly surrounded by . . . 3.	The Greeks used the seas for transportation.
Greece produced surplus . . . 4. 5. 6. 7.	Greeks traded these items to other regions for grain, timber, and animal hides.

SECTION 1: THE GEOGRAPHY OF GREECE, *CONTINUED*

Causes	Effects
Although the cause is unknown, invaders might have been responsible.	8. . . . civilization collapsed around 1200 B.C.
The Greeks traded with the Phoenicians.	Between 900 and 800 B.C., the Greeks began using the Phoenician . . . 9.
The Greeks traded with . . . 10. where coins were invented about 650 B.C..	Most parts of . . . 11. were making their own coins by 500 B.C.

MARK IT UP! Circle each term where it appears in your notes and be sure you understand its meaning. If a term does not appear, write it beside the box where it best belongs.	peninsula Phoenicians Peloponnesus alphabet isthmus

SKILLBUILDER

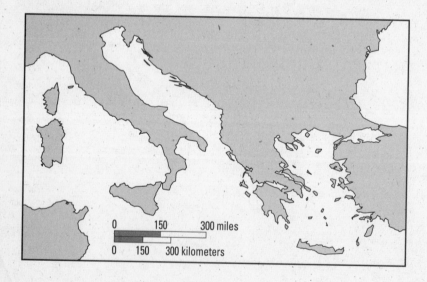

0 150 300 miles

0 150 300 kilometers

12. ***MARK IT UP!*** Label the Peloponnesus.

13. ***MARK IT UP!*** Label the Ionian and Aegean Seas.

14. Describe two ways that the ancient Greeks used the seas.

_____

_____

_____

Date

SECTION

2 | Life in Ancient Greece

READING STUDY GUIDE

- **Before, You Learned** The life of ancient Greeks was influenced by Greece's geography and trade.

- **Now You Will Learn** The ancient Greeks honored many gods and developed their own literature.

AS YOU READ Take notes making generalizations about life in ancient Greece. Use the following graphic organizers.

Greek Religious Beliefs	Greek Literature
The Greeks told stories about the gods.	1. Later, these stories might be written down. They are called . . .
The Greeks developed myths to explain the creation of the world.	2. When Pandora opened the jar that Zeus had given her, sickness, greed, and all the other evils escaped. What remained in the jar was . . .
The gods influence human events.	3. In the *Odyssey*, Odysseus offends the god of the sea, . . .

CHAPTER 7

SECTION 2: LIFE IN ANCIENT GREECE, *CONTINUED*

God or Goddess	Way of Honoring
4.	A new robe was woven for her statue in the main temple.
Zeus	5.
6.	Unmarried girls competed in foot races in the Olympic stadium.

MARK IT UP! Circle each term where it appears in your notes and be sure you understand its meaning. If a term does not appear, write it beside the box where it best belongs.

Zeus	Olympics
Mount Olympus	epics
myths	fable

SKILLBUILDER

Primary Source

But now, Achilles, beat down your mounting fury!
It's wrong to have such an iron, ruthless heart.
Even the gods themselves can bend and change,
and theirs is the greater power, honor, strength.

Homer, the *Iliad*, Book IX

7. **MARK IT UP!** Underline the words that describe the human qualities of the gods.

8. **MARK IT UP!** Circle the name of the hero to whom this statement is addressed.

9. How does Achilles feel? What does the speaker want Achilles to do?

_____

_____

SECTION
3

READING STUDY GUIDE

The City-State and Democracy

- **Before, You Learned** The Greeks honored many gods and developed their own literature.

- **Now You Will Learn** The growth of city-states in Greece led to the development of different political systems, including democracy.

AS YOU READ Take notes categorizing what you learn about the different forms of government. Use the following graphic organizers.

Types of Government		
Monarchy	Oligarchy	Democracy
1. A monarch is . . .	3. Oligarchy means . . .	5. Democracy is a form of government in which . . .
2. Most Greek city-states started out . . .	4. In oligarchies, people rule because of . . .	6. The Athenian style of democracy is called . . .

CHAPTER 7

Athenian Democracy		
Direct Democracy	Citizenship	Citizens' Responsibilities
7. In direct democracy, the citizens meet to decide on . . .	9. In Athens, citizenship was limited to . . .	11. During times of war, Athenian citizens had to . . .
8. In representative democracy, laws are made by . . .	10. When a person was ostracized, he or she had to . . .	12. Citizens who were at least 30 years old had to . . .

MARK IT UP! Circle each term where it appears in your notes and be sure you understand its meaning. If a term does not appear, write it beside the box where it best belongs.	polis aristocracy oligarchy	tyrant democracy ostracize

SKILLBUILDER

Primary Source

To the mass of the people I gave the
    power they needed,
Neither degrading them, nor giving
    them too much rein.
For those who already possessed
    great power and wealth
I saw to it that their interests were
    not harmed.
I stood guard with a broad shield
    before both parties
And prevented either from
    triumphing unjustly.

From poem by Solon quoted in "Life of Solon,"
*The Rise and Fall of Athens: Nine Greek Lives by
Plutarch*, translated by Ian Scott-Kilvert, New
York Penguin, 1960.

13. ***MARK IT UP!*** Underline the lines that show how Solon helped the common Athenians.

14. ***MARK IT UP!*** Circle the lines that describe how Solon balanced the interests of the rich and the commoners.

15. What might have happened if Solon had not "stood guard with a broad shield"?

_____

_____

_____

SECTION
4 | READING STUDY GUIDE
Sparta and Athens

- **Before, You Learned** Athens developed a direct, though limited, democracy in which citizens made political decisions.

- **Now You Will Learn** Sparta's government developed around its strong army. Several city-states united to defeat the invading Persians.

AS YOU READ Take notes listing the similarities and differences between Athens and Sparta. Also note facts about battles in the Persian Wars. Use the graphic organizers on the following pages.

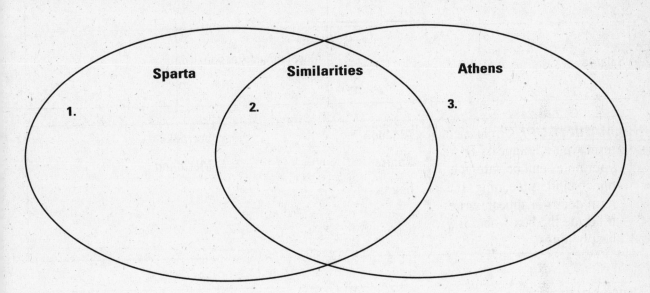

Sparta   Similarities   Athens

1.   2.   3.

SECTION 4: SPARTA AND ATHENS, *CONTINUED*

Battles of the Persian Wars			
Battle	Year	Who Fought?	Who Won?
Marathon	4.	5.	6.
7.	480 B.C.	8.	9.
Salamis	10.	Athenian and Persian navies	11.

MARK IT UP! Circle each term where it appears in your notes and be sure you understand its meaning. If a term does not appear, write it beside the box where it best belongs.	Athens barracks Sparta Marathon helots

SKILLBUILDER

Source: *Combat scene, a wounded or dead hoplite lies on the ground* (560–550 B.C.), Cleimachos. Pottery. Louvre, Paris. Photo © Erich Lessing/Art Resource, New York.

12. **MARK IT UP!** Outline the fallen soldier in this picture.

13. Write a caption describing a battle between the Greeks and the Persians.

_____

_____

_____

SECTION

1

READING STUDY GUIDE WITH ADDITIONAL SUPPORT

The Geography of Greece

Before, You Learned

The geography of China influenced the ancient cultures that developed there.

Now You Will Learn

The geography of Greece led to sea travel and trade, which influenced Greek culture.

Preview Terms and Names

- **peninsula:** land with water on three sides
- **Peloponnesus:** (PEHL•uh•puh•NEE•suhs) peninsula that forms the southern part of Greece
- **isthmus:** (IHS•muhs) narrow strip of land
- **Phoenicians:** (fih•NISH•uhnz) people of Southwest Asia who began to trade around 1100 B.C.
- **alphabet:** system of symbols representing sounds

Take Notes as You Read

Use this chart to take notes as you read.

Causes	1. Effects
Mountains cover most of Greece.	a. The Greeks had difficulty . . .
Several seas surround Greece.	b. The Greeks used the seas as . . .
Greece traded with other regions.	c. Traders came into contact with people who lived around . . .

Geography Shapes Ancient Greek Life

The mainland of Greece is a peninsula that extends out into the Mediterranean Sea. Its southern tip forms a second peninsula called the Peloponnesus. Mountains divided ancient Greece into many regions and made transportation difficult. Most farming took place in the valleys between the mountains. In order to get more farmland, the Greeks founded colonies in other regions, such as Anatolia.

The warm climate encouraged outdoor life and athletic competition in ancient Greece.

2. How did the landscape affect ancient Greek life?

_____

_____

Trade Helps Greece Prosper

The difficulties of overland travel encouraged the Greeks to use the seas as transportation routes. The Greeks built warships and sailing ships for trading.

CHAPTER 7

SECTION 1: THE GEOGRAPHY OF GREECE, *CONTINUED*

Some regions of Greece produced surplus olive oil, wine, wool, and fine pottery. Greeks traded these items to other regions around the Black Sea and the Mediterranean Sea, including Egypt and Italy.

3. What trade goods did the Greeks produce?

_____

_____

The Earliest Greeks

The earliest Greeks had moved onto the Greek peninsula by about 2000 B.C. The first Greek civilization was built on the Peloponnesus. It was named after its most important city, Mycenae. Mycenaean culture featured writing, gold jewelry, bronze weapons, and fine pottery.

The civilization collapsed around 1200 B.C., and the Greeks stopped keeping written records. Without such records, little is known about the period from 1200 to 750 B.C.

In time, Greek culture began to revive. The Greeks developed an alphabet, thanks to their contact with the alphabet used by Phoenician traders. From trading with other peoples, the Greeks also learned about the practice of using coins as money.

4. What happened after the collapse of Mycenaean civilization?

_____

_____

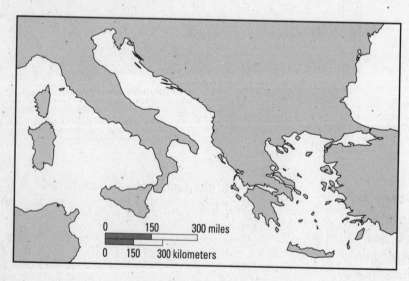

Mark It Up!

5. Label Greece.

6. Circle the Peloponnesus.

SECTION 2

READING STUDY GUIDE WITH ADDITIONAL SUPPORT

Life in Ancient Greece

Before, You Learned

The life of ancient Greeks was influenced by Greece's geography and trade.

Now You Will Learn

The ancient Greeks honored many gods and developed their own literature.

Preview Terms and Names

- **Zeus:** ruler of the greek gods
- **Mount Olympus:** highest mountain in Greece; gods were believed to have lived there
- **myths:** stories that people tell to explain beliefs about their world
- **Olympics:** games held every four years
- **epics:** long poems about ancient heroes
- **fable:** short story that usually involves animals and teaches a moral

Take Notes as You Read

Use this chart to take notes as you read.

Greek Religious Beliefs	1. Greek Literature
The Greeks told stories about the gods.	a. Later, these stories might be written down. They are called . . .
It was important to honor the gods.	b. Games held every four years as part of a festival to honor Zeus were called . . .
The gods influence human events.	c. In the *Odyssey*, Odysseus offends the god . . .

Greek Gods and Myths

The Greek gods had both divine and human qualities. They were very powerful, but they had human emotions such as love and anger.

Zeus was the ruler of the gods. The Greeks believed that he and 11 other major gods and goddesses lived on Mount Olympus, the highest mountain in Greece. Each city worshiped one of the gods or goddesses as its protector.

The Greeks created myths to explain the creation of the world and of human beings. Other myths portrayed Greek heroes and heroines.

2. What characteristics did the Greek gods have?

_____

_____

_____

SECTION 2: LIFE IN ANCIENT GREECE, *CONTINUED*

Honoring the Gods

The Greeks believed it was important to honor the gods. They built temples as places for the gods to live. People celebrated holy days with sacrifices and public ceremonies. They also staged games, poetry recitals, and other events to honor the gods. The Olympics were games held every four years as part of a major festival that honored Zeus.

3. What was the purpose of the Olympics?

_____

_____

Early Greek Literature

The Greeks also composed long poems, known as epics, that told stories about gods and

_____

heroes. According to tradition, a blind man named Homer composed the most famous epics, called the *Iliad* and the *Odyssey*. The backdrop of both poems is the Trojan War.

Another famous work of Greek literature is a collection of stories known as Aesop's Fables. A fable is a short story, usually involving animals, that teaches a moral lesson and sometimes offers advice.

4. What event forms the backdrop to both the *Iliad* and the *Odyssey*?

_____

_____

Primary Source

But now, Achilles, beat down your mounting fury!
It's wrong to have such an iron, ruthless heart.
Even the gods themselves can bend and change,
and theirs is the greater power, honor, strength.

Homer, the *Iliad*, Book IX

5. **Underline** the words that describe the human qualities of the gods.

SECTION

3 | READING STUDY GUIDE WITH ADDITIONAL SUPPORT
The City-State and Democracy

Before, You Learned

The Greeks honored many gods and developed their own literature.

Now You Will Learn

The growth of city-states in Greece led to the development of different political systems, including democracy.

 **Preview** Terms and Names

- **polis:** Greek word for city-state
- **aristocracy:** (AR•ih•STAHK•ruh•see) rule by the upper classes
- **oligarchy:** (AHL•ih•GAHR•kee) rule by the few
- **tyrant:** ruler who takes power illegally
- **citizen:** person who is loyal to and protected by a government
- **democracy:** government in which citizens make political decisions either directly or through elected representatives

 **Take Notes as You Read**

Use this chart to take notes as you read.

1. Types of Government		
Monarchy	Oligarchy	Democracy
a. A monarch is . . .	c. Oligarchy means . . .	e. Democracy is a form of government in which . . .
b. Most Greek city-states started out . . .	d. In an oligarchy, people rule because of . . .	f. The Athenian style of democracy is called . . .

The Rise of City-States

The mountainous geography of Greece made political unity difficult in ancient times. Instead, many small city-states developed. The center of city life was the agora, an open space where people came for business and public gatherings. Many cities had a fortified hilltop called an acropolis. At first, the acropolis was used for military purposes. Later, the Greeks built temples and palaces on the flat tops of these hills.

2. How did Greece's geography affect political unity?

_____

_____

Forms of Government

Most of the Greek city-states started as monarchies, in which a king or queen rules. By the 700s B.C., most had become aristocracies, ruled by members of the nobility.

CHAPTER 7

SECTION 3: THE CITY-STATE AND DEMOCRACY, *CONTINUED*

Some city-states developed a political system called oligarchy, which means "rule by the few." In an oligarchy, only the wealthy rule.

Sometimes a tyrant gained control of a city-state. A tyrant was someone who took power illegally and ruled like a king. Tyrants helped to pave the way for rule by the people.

3. What political systems were used in Greek city-states?

_____

_____

Athens Builds a Limited Democracy

During the 500s B.C., the political leaders Solon and Cleisthenes made gradual reforms that gave common Athenians more power. Solon

_____

allowed all citizens to serve in the assembly, the law-making body. Cleisthenes reorganized the assembly to take power away from the nobles.

Athens became a democracy, a government ruled by its citizens. Athens had a direct democracy, which means that the citizens themselves—not elected representatives—decided on the laws. However, citizenship was limited to free adult males. Athenian citizens had to serve in the army when necessary. They also served on juries.

4. Which rulers helped give the Athenian people more power?

_____

_____

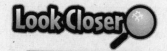

5. Underline the lines that show how Solon helped the common Athenians.

Primary Source

To the mass of the people I gave the power they
   needed,
Neither degrading them, nor giving them too much
   rein.
For those who already possessed great power and
   wealth
I saw to it that their interests were not harmed.
I stood guard with a broad shield before both parties
And prevented either from triumphing unjustly.

From poem by Solon quoted in "Life of Solon," *The Rise and Fall of Athens: Nine Greek Lives by Plutarch*, translated by Ian Scott-Kilvert, New York Penguin, 1960.

SECTION
4 | READING STUDY GUIDE WITH ADDITIONAL SUPPORT
Sparta and Athens

Before, You Learned

Athens developed a direct, though limited, democracy in which citizens made political decisions.

Now You Will Learn

Sparta's government developed around its strong army. Several city-states united to defeat the invading Persians.

Preview Terms and Names

- **Athens:** city-state of ancient Greece, noted for its democratic form of government
- **Sparta:** city-state of ancient Greece, noted for its militarism
- **helots (HEHL•uhtz):** enslaved people of Sparta
- **barracks:** military houses
- **Marathon:** plain near Athens

Use this chart to take notes as you read.

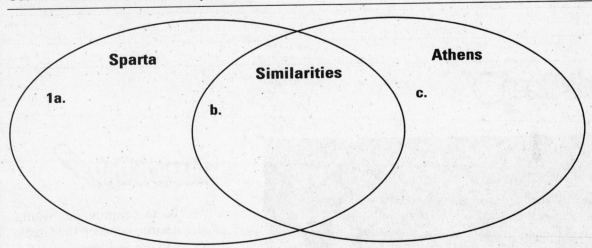

Sparta's Military State

About 715 B.C., Sparta conquered a neighboring area and enslaved its people, who became known as helots. Fear of helot revolts led Sparta to focus on building a strong army. Sparta's government was part monarchy, part oligarchy, and part democracy.

At age seven, Spartan boys moved into military houses called barracks and began receiving military training. Men entered the army at the age of 20 and served until they were

60. Education for girls focused on making them physically strong. Spartan women had more freedom than in other city-states.

2. How were Spartan boys educated?

_____

_____

SECTION 4: SPARTA AND ATHENS, *CONTINUED*

Athens' Democratic Way of Life

As Athens developed into a democracy, its people focused on government matters. Athenians were divided into four main classes—citizens, women, non-citizen free persons, and enslaved people. Enslaved people made up one-third of the population.

Boys of wealthy families started school at age six or seven. Their education was designed to make them into good citizens. Girls did not attend school, but learned household duties from their mothers. Athenian women were respected for their roles as wives and mothers, but they had less freedom than Spartan women.

3. What was the goal of education for Athenian boys?

_____

_____

The Persian Wars

In 490 B.C. a Persian army arrived in Greece. The Persians wanted to punish the Athenians for helping Greeks in Anatolia revolt against Persian rule. On the plain of Marathon, near Athens, the Greeks defeated the Persians. Legend says that a soldier ran 25 miles from Marathon to Athens to tell of the victory. Modern marathons are named after this event.

In 480 B.C., Persia again invaded Greece. Several city-states united against Persia. An army of 300 Spartans died at the narrow pass at Thermopylae to stop the Persians from reaching Athens. Later, the Athenians defeated the Persians during a naval battle.

4. Why did the Spartans die at Thermopylae?

_____

_____

Look Closer

Source: *Combat scene, a wounded or dead hoplite lies on the ground* (560–550 B.C.), Cleimachos. Pottery. Louvre, Paris. Photo © Erich Lessing/Art Resource, New York.

Mark It Up!

5. Write a caption describing a battle between the Greeks and the Persians.

_____

_____

_____

GUÍA DE ESTUDIO DE LECTURA

La geografía de Grecia

- **Antes aprendiste** La geografía de China tuvo influencia sobre las culturas antiguas que se desarrollaron allí.

- **Ahora aprenderás** La geografía de Grecia dio lugar a los viajes y al comercio marítimos, lo cual tuvo influencia en la cultura griega.

AL LEER Toma notas donde enumeres las causas y los efectos presentados en la sección. Usa las siguientes ayudas gráficas de causas y efectos.

Causas	Efectos
Las montañas cubren la mayor parte de Grecia.	Los griegos tenían dificultades en [...] 1. 2.
Grecia está prácticamente rodeada de [...] 3.	Los griegos utilizaban los mares como vías de transporte.
Grecia producía un excedente de [...] 4. 5. 6. 7.	Los griegos comerciaban estos artículos con otras regiones a cambio de granos, madera y pieles de animales.

SECCIÓN 1: LA GEOGRAFÍA DE GRECIA, *CONTINUACIÓN*

Causas	Efectos
Si bien la causa es desconocida, los invasores podrían haber sido los responsables.	8. La civilización [...] colapsó alrededor del año 1200. a.C.
Los griegos comerciaban con los fenicios.	Entre los años 900 y 800 a.C., los griegos comenzaron a utilizar el [...] fenicio. 9.
Los griegos comerciaban con [...] 10. donde las monedas se inventaron alrededor del año 650 a.C..	Gran parte de [...] 11. fabricaban sus propias monedas hacia el año 500 a.C.

¡MÁRCALO! Encierra en un círculo cada término cuando aparezca en tus notas y asegúrate de entender su significado. Si un término no aparece, escríbelo junto al recuadro que mejor le corresponda.	**península** **Peloponeso** **istmo**	**fenicios** **alfabeto**

DESARROLLAR DESTREZAS

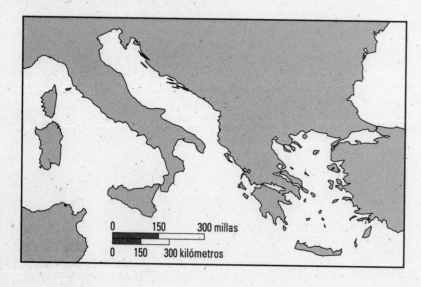

0   150   300 millas
0   150   300 kilómetros

12. **¡MÁRCALO!** Pon título al Peloponeso.

13. **¡MÁRCALO!** Pon título a los mares Jónico y Egeo.

14. Describe dos maneras de aprovechar los antiguos griegos los mares.

_____

_____

_____

SECCIÓN

2

GUÍA DE ESTUDIO DE LECTURA
La vida en la antigua Grecia

- **Antes aprendiste** La vida de los antiguos griegos se vio influenciada por la geografía de Grecia y por el comercio.

- **Ahora aprenderás** Los antiguos griegos adoraban a muchos dioses y fomentaron su propia literatura.

AL LEER Toma notas para hacer generalizaciones acerca de la vida en la antigua Grecia. Usa las ayudas gráficas siguientes.

Creencias religiosas griegas	Literatura griega
Los griegos relataban historias sobre los dioses.	1. Luego, estas historias se habrían puesto por escrito. Se denominan [...]
Los griegos crearon mitos para explicar la creación del mundo.	2. Cuando Pandora abrió el ánfora, o cántaro, que Zeus le había dado, escaparon la enfermedad, la codicia y todos los otros males. Lo que quedó en el ánfora fue [...]
Los dioses tienen influencia sobre los sucesos humanos.	3. En la *Odisea*, Ulises ofende al dios del mar, [...]

CHAPTER 7

SECCIÓN 2: LA VIDA EN LA ANTIGUA GRECIA, *CONTINUACIÓN*

Dios o diosa	Forma de culto
4.	Una túnica nueva se tejió para su estatua, colocada en el templo principal.
Zeus	5.
6.	Las jóvenes solteras competían en carreras a pie en el estadio olímpico.

¡MÁRCALO! Encierra en un círculo cada término cuando aparezca en tus notas y asegúrate de entender su significado. Si un término no aparece, escríbelo junto al recuadro que mejor le corresponda.	**Zeus** **monte Olimpo** **mitos**	**Olimpíadas** **poemas épicos** **fábula**

DESARROLLAR DESTREZAS

Fuente primaria

Pero ahora, Aquiles, ¡desiste de tu furia
    creciente!

Es malo tener un corazón tan férreo y
    brutal.

Incluso los mismos dioses pueden ceder
    y cambiar,

y a ellos pertenece el mayor poder, el
    honor y la fuerza.

Homero, la *Ilíada*, Libro IX

7. ¡MÁRCALO! Subraya las palabras que describen las características humanas de los dioses.

8. ¡MÁRCALO! Encierra en un círculo el nombre del héroe a quien se dirige esta afirmación.

9. ¿Cómo se siente Aquiles? ¿Qué quiere el hablante que haga Aquiles?

_____

_____

SECCIÓN
3

GUÍA DE ESTUDIO DE LECTURA
La ciudad estado y la democracia

- **Antes aprendiste** Los antiguos griegos honraban a muchos dioses y desarrollaron su propia literatura.

- **Ahora aprenderás** El crecimiento de las ciudades estado griegas llevó al desarrollo de diversos sistemas políticos, incluida la democracia.

AL LEER Toma notas para categorizar lo que aprendiste acerca de las diferentes formas de gobierno. Usa las ayudas gráficas siguientes.

Formas de gobierno		
Monarquía	Oligarquía	Democracia
1. Un monarca es [...]	3. Oligarquía significa [...]	5. La democracia es una forma de gobierno en la cual [...]
2. La mayoría de las ciudades estado griegas comenzaron [...]	4. En las oligarquías, la gente gobierna por [...]	6. El estilo ateniense de democracia se denomina [...]

Name

Date

Democracia ateniense		
Democracia directa	Ciudadanía	Responsabilidades de los ciudadanos
7. En la democracia directa, los ciudadanos se reúnen para decidir sobre [...]	9. En Atenas, la ciudadanía estaba limitada a [...]	11. Durante los tiempos de guerra, los ciudadanos atenienses debían [...]
8. En la democracia representativa, las leyes son hechas por [...]	10. Cuando una persona era desterrada, tenía que [...]	12. Los ciudadanos que tenían al menos 30 años de edad debían [...]

¡MÁRCALO! Encierra en un círculo cada término cuando aparezca en tus notas y asegúrate de entender su significado. Si un término no aparece, escríbelo junto al recuadro que mejor le corresponda.	polis	tirano
	aristocracia	democracia
	oligarquía	desterrar

DESARROLLAR DESTREZAS

Fuente primaria

A la masa del pueblo di el poder que
    necesitaban,
ni degradándolos, ni dándoles
    demasiado control.
Para aquéllos que ya poseían grandes
    poderes y riquezas
cuidé que sus intereses no fueran
    dañados.
Me mantuve en pie colocando un amplio
    escudo frente a ambos partidos
y evité que cualquiera de los dos
    triunfara injustamente.

De un poema de Solón citado en "Vida de Solón",
*El ascenso y la caída de Atenas: Nueve vidas
griegas, por Plutarco* , traducido al inglés por Ian
Scott-Kilvert, New York Penguin, 1960.

13. **¡MÁRCALO!**   Subraya los versos que muestran cómo Solón ayudó a los ciudadanos atenienses.

14. **¡MÁRCALO!**   Encierra los versos que describen cómo Solón equilibró los intereses de los ricos y de los plebeyos.

15. ¿Qué habría sucedido si Solón no se hubiera mantenido "en pie colocando un amplio escudo"?

_____

_____

_____

SECCIÓN
4

GUÍA DE ESTUDIO DE LECTURA
Esparta y Atenas

- **Antes aprendiste** Atenas desarrolló una democracia directa, aunque limitada, en la cual los ciudadanos tomaban las decisiones políticas.

- **Ahora aprenderás** El gobierno de Esparta se desarrolló por medio de un poderoso ejército. Varias ciudades estado se unieron para derrotar a los invasores persas.

AL LEER Toma notas que enumeren las semejanzas y las diferencias entre Atenas y Esparta. También anota datos sobre las batallas de las Guerras Persas. Usa las ayudas gráficas de las páginas siguientes.

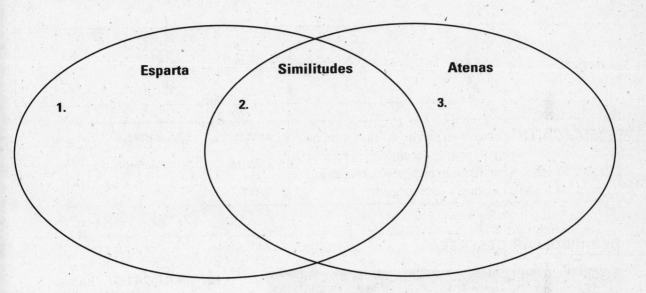

Esparta

Similitudes

Atenas

1.

2.

3.

SECCIÓN 4: ESPARTA Y ATENAS, *CONTINUACIÓN*

Batallas de las Guerras Persas			
Batalla	Año	¿Quiénes lucharon?	¿Quién venció?
Maratón	4.	5.	6.
7.	480 a.C.	8.	9.
Salamina	10.	flotas ateniense y persa	11.

¡MÁRCALO! Encierra en un círculo cada término cuando aparezca en tus notas y asegúrate de entender su significado. Si un término no aparece, escríbelo junto al recuadro que mejor le corresponda.	Atenas · · · · · · · barracas Esparta · · · · · · · Maratón ilotas

DESARROLLAR DESTREZAS

Source: *Combat scene, a wounded or dead hoplite lies on the ground* (560–550 B.C.), Cleimachos. Pottery. Louvre, Paris. Photo © Erich Lessing/Art Resource, New York.

12. ¡MÁRCALO! En esta imagen, traza el contorno del soldado caído.

13. Escribe un calce que describa una batalla entre los griegos y los persas.

_____

_____

_____

SECCIÓN 1

GUÍA DE ESTUDIO DE LECTURA CON APOYO ADICIONAL

La geografía de Grecia

Antes aprendiste

La geografía de China influyó en las culturas antiguas que se desarrollaron allí.

Ahora aprenderás

La geografía de Grecia fomentó el transporte marítimo y el comercio, lo cual influyó en la cultura griega.

Vistazo previo a Términos y nombres

- **península:** tierra rodeada por agua en tres de sus lados
- **Peloponeso:** península que forma la parte sur de Grecia
- **istmo:** franja estrecha de tierra
- **fenicios:** pueblos del suroeste de Asia que empezó a comerciar alrededor del año 1100 a.C.
- **alfabeto:** sistema de símbolos que representan sonidos

Tomar notas al leer

Usa este diagrama para tomar notas mientras lees.

Causas	Efectos
Las montañas cubren la mayor parte de Grecia.	1. Los griegos tenían dificultadespara unir . . .
Varios mares rodean a Grecia.	2. Los griegos usaron los marespara . . .
Grecia comerciaba con otras regiones.	3. Los mercaderes entraron en contacto con pueblos que vivíanalrededor del . . .

La geografía da forma a la vida de la antigua Grecia

La parte continental de Grecia es una península que se prolonga hacia el interior del mar Mediterráneo. Su extremo sur forma una segunda península denominada Peloponeso. Las montañas dividían a la antigua Grecia en muchas regiones y hacían difícil el transporte. La mayor parte de la agricultura tenía lugar en los valles entre las montañas. Con el fin de obtener más tierra de cultivo, los griegos fundaron colonias en otras regiones, como Anatolia.

En la antigua Grecia, el clima cálido fomentó la vida al aire libre y las competencias de atletismo.

4. ¿De qué manera el paisaje afectó la vida en la antigua Grecia?

_____

_____

El comercio contribuye a la prosperidad de Grecia

Las dificultades para viajar por tierra incentivaron a los griegos a emplear los mares como rutas de transporte. Los griegos construyeron barcos de guerra y veleros para comerciar.

Algunas regiones de Grecia producían un excedente de aceite de oliva, vino, lana y objetos finos de alfarería. Los griegos comerciaban

SECCIÓN 1: LA GEOGRAFÍA DE GRECIA, *CONTINUACIÓN*

estos artículos con otras regiones que se hallaban alrededor del mar Negro y del mar Mediterráneo, incluidos Egipto e Italia.

5. ¿Qué artículos comerciales producían los griegos?

_____

_____

Los primeros griegos

Los primeros griegos habían llegado a la península griega alrededor del año 2000 a.C. La primera civilización griega se desarrolló en el Peloponeso. Recibió el nombre de su ciudad más importante, Micenas. La cultura micénica se destacó por su escritura, su joyería de oro, sus armas de bronce y sus finos objetos de alfarería.

La civilización colapsó alrededor del año 1200 a.C. y los griegos dejaron de llevar registros escritos. Sin tales registros, poco se sabe acerca del período que va desde el año 1200 al año 750 a.C.

Con el transcurso del tiempo, la cultura griega empezó a revivir. Los griegos desarrollaron un alfabeto gracias a su contacto con el alfabeto utilizado por los mercaderes fenicios. Del comercio con otros pueblos, los griegos también aprendieron la práctica de usar monedas como dinero.

6. ¿Qué sucedió después del colapso de la civilización micénica?

_____

_____

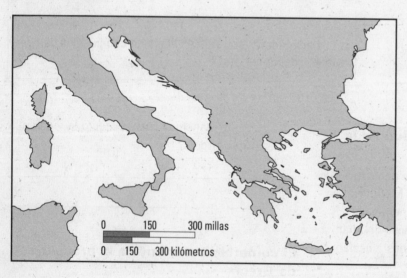

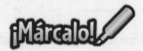

7. Rotula el Peloponeso.

Date

SECCIÓN
2

GUÍA DE ESTUDIO DE LECTURA CON APOYO ADICIONAL
La vida en la antigua Grecia

Antes aprendiste

La vida de los antiguos griegos estuvo influenciada por la geografía de Grecia y por el comercio.

Ahora aprenderás

Los antiguos griegos adoraban a muchos dioses y desarrollaron su propia literatura.

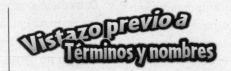

Vistazo previo a Términos y nombres

- **Zeus:** dios supremo de los griegos
- **Monte Olimpo:** la montaña más alta de Grecia, donde se creía que vivían los dioses griegos
- **mitos:** relatos que cuentan las personas para explicar creencias acerca de su mundo
- **Olimpíadas:** juegos llevados a cabo cada cuatro años
- **épicas:** poemas extensos acerca de las aventuras de los héroes
- **fábula:** narración corta que usualmente incluye personajes animales y transmite una enseñanza moral

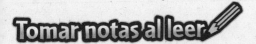

Tomar notas al leer Utiliza este diagrama para tomar notas mientras lees.

Creencias religiosas griegas	1. Literatura griega
Los griegos contaban relatos acerca de los dioses.	a. Posteriormente, estos relatos fueron puestos por escrito. Se denominan [...]
Era importante honrar a los dioses.	b. Los juegos realizados cada cuatro años como parte de un festival en honor a Zeus se llamaban [...]
Los dioses tienen influencia sobre los sucesos humanos.	c. En la *Odisea*, Odiseo ofende al dios [...]

Dioses y mitos griegos

Los dioses griegos tenían atributos tanto divinos como humanos. Eran muy poderosos, pero sentían emociones humanas, como el amor y la ira.

Zeus era la divinidad suprema. Los griegos creían que él y otros once dioses y diosas vivían en el Monte Olimpo, la montaña más alta de Grecia. Cada ciudad adoraba a uno de los dioses o diosas como su protector o protectora.

Los griegos crearon mitos para explicar la creación del mundo y de los seres humanos. Otros mitos presentaban a heroínas y héroes griegos.

2. ¿Qué características tenían los dioses griegos?

_____

_____

SECCIÓN 2: LA VIDA EN LA ANTIGUA GRECIA, *CONTINUACIÓN*

Honrar a los dioses

Los griegos creían que era importante honrar a los dioses. Construyeron templos para que los dioses los habitaran. Las personas celebraban los días sagrados con sacrificios y ceremonias públicas. También realizaban juegos, recitales de poesía y otros eventos para honrar a los dioses. Las Olimpíadas eran juegos que se llevaban a cabo cada cuatro años como parte de la festividad principal en honor a Zeus.

3. ¿Cuál era el propósito de las Olimpíadas?

_____

_____

La antigua literatura griega

Los griegos también compusieron extensos poemas, denominados poemas épicos, que

_____

relataban historias acerca de dioses y héroes. Según la tradición, un ciego llamado Homero compuso los poemas épicos más famosos, titulados la *Ilíada* y la *Odisea*. El escenario de ambos poemas es la Guerra de Troya.

Otra obra famosa de la literatura griega es una colección de cuentos conocidos como las Fábulas de Esopo. Una fábula es un relato breve, donde generalmente aparecen animales, que transmite una enseñanza moral y a veces proporciona un consejo.

4. ¿Qué suceso forma el escenario de la *Ilíada* y la *Odisea*?

_____

_____

Fuente primaria

Pero ahora, Aquiles, ¡desiste de tu furia creciente!
Es malo tener un corazón tan férreo y brutal.
Incluso los mismos dioses pueden ceder y cambiar,
y a ellos pertenece el mayor poder, el honor y la fuerza.

Homero, la *Ilíada*, Libro IX

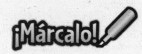

5. Subraya las palabras que describen los atributos humanos de los dioses.

GUÍA DE ESTUDIO DE LECTURA CON APOYO ADICIONAL
La ciudad estado y la democracia

Antes aprendiste

Los griegos honraban a muchos dioses y desarrollaron su propia literatura.

Ahora aprenderás

El crecimiento de las ciudades estado griegas llevó al desarrollo de diversos sistemas políticos, incluida la democracia.

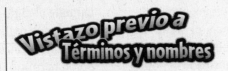
Vistazo previo a Términos y nombres

- **polis:** palabra griega para designar a la ciudad estado
- **aristocracia:** un gobierno ejercido por las clases altas
- **oligarquía:** un gobierno ejercido por unos pocos individuos poderosos
- **tirano:** un gobernante que ha tomado el poder en forma ilegal
- **ciudadano:** persona que debe lealtad a un país y recibe su protección
- **democracia:** gobierno en el cual los ciudadanos toman las decisiones políticas, ya sea en forma directa o mediante representantes elegidos por el pueblo

Tomar notas al leer

Utiliza este diagrama para tomar notas mientras lees.

1. Tipos de gobierno		
Monarquía	Oligarquía	Democracia
a. Un monarca es [...]	**c.** Oligarquía significa [...]	**e.** La democracia es una forma de gobierno en la cual [...]
b. La mayoría de las ciudades estado griegas comenzaron [...]	**d.** En una oligarquía, las personas gobiernan debido a [...]	**f.** El estilo ateniense de democracia se denomina [...]

El surgimiento de las ciudades estado

En la antigüedad, la geografía montañosa de Grecia dificultó su unidad política. En cambio, se desarrollaron muchas ciudades estado pequeñas. El centro de la vida de la ciudad era el ágora, un espacio abierto donde se encontraban las personas para realizar negocios y reuniones públicas, como asambleas. Muchas ciudades habían fortificado la cima de una colina, llamada acrópolis. Al principio, las acrópolis se empleaban con propósitos militares.

Posteriormente, los griegos construyeron templos y palacios sobre las cimas planas de estas colinas.

2. ¿De qué manera la geografía de Grecia afectó a su unidad política?

_____

_____

SECCIÓN 3: LA CIUDAD ESTADO Y LA DEMOCRACIA, *CONTINUACIÓN*

Formas de gobierno

La mayoría de las ciudades estado griegas comenzaron como monarquías, en las cuales gobierna un rey o una reina. Hacia el siglo VIII a.C., la mayoría se habían convertido en aristocracias, dirigidas por miembros de la nobleza.

Algunas de estas ciudades estado desarrollaron un sistema político llamado oligarquía, que significa "gobierno de unos pocos". En una oligarquía, sólo gobiernan los ricos.

A veces, un tirano tomaba el control de una ciudad estado. Un tirano era alguien que tomaba el poder ilegalmente y gobernaba como si fuera un rey. Los tiranos contribuyeron a abrir el camino para el gobierno por el pueblo.

3. ¿Qué sistemas políticos se emplearon en las ciudades estado griegas?

_____

_____

Atenas construye una democracia limitada

Durante el siglo VI a.C., los líderes políticos Solón y Clístenes realizaron reformas graduales que concedieron más poder a los atenienses comunes. Solón permitió que todos los ciudadanos sirvieran en la asamblea, el cuerpo legislativo. Clístenes reorganizó la asamblea para quitarle el poder a los nobles.

Atenas se convirtió en una democracia, un gobierno dirigido por sus ciudadanos. Atenas tenía una democracia directa, lo cual significa que los ciudadanos mismos, no los representantes elegidos, decidían con respecto a las leyes. Sin embargo, la ciudadanía estaba limitada a los varones adultos libres. Los ciudadanos atenienses tenían que servir en el ejército cuando era necesario. También servían en los jurados.

4. ¿Qué gobernantes contribuyeron a que el pueblo ateniense obtuviera más poder?

_____

_____

De cerca

Fuente primaria

A la masa del pueblo di el poder que necesitaban,

Ni degradándolos, ni dándoles demasiado control.

Para aquéllos que ya poseían grandes poderes y riquezas

Cuidé que sus intereses no fueran dañados.

Me mantuve en pie colocando un amplio escudo frente a
    ambos partidos

Y evité que cualquiera de los dos triunfara injustamente.

De un poema de Solón citado en "Vida de Solón", *El ascenso y la caída de Atenas: Nueve vidas griegas por Plutarco*, traducido al inglés por Ian Scott-Kilvert, New York Penguin, 1960.

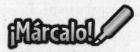

5. Subraya los versos que muestran de qué manera Solón ayudó a los atenienses comunes.

SECCIÓN

4

GUÍA DE ESTUDIO DE LECTURA CON APOYO ADICIONAL

Esparta y Atenas

Antes aprendiste

Atenas desarrolló una democracia directa, aunque limitada, en la cual los ciudadanos tomaban las decisiones políticas.

Ahora aprenderás

El gobierno de Esparta se desarrolló alrededor de su fuerte ejército. Varias ciudades estado se unieron para derrotar a los invasores persas.

Vistazo previo a Términos y nombres

- **Atenas:** ciudad estado de la antigua Grecia, famosa por su forma democrática de gobierno
- **Esparta:** ciudad estado de la antigua Grecia, caracterizada por su militarismo
- **ilotas:** habitantes esclavizados de Esparta
- **barracas:** viviendas militares
- **Maratón:** llanura cercana a Atenas

Tomar notas al leer

Utiliza este diagrama para tomar notas mientras lees.

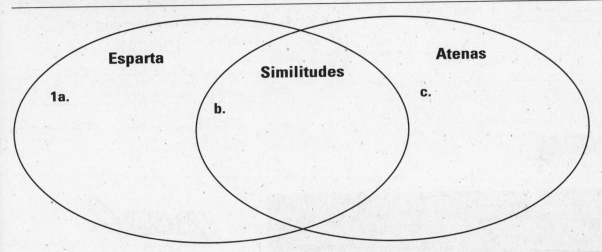

Esparta — 1a.

Similitudes — b.

Atenas — c.

El estado militar de Esparta

Alrededor del año 715 a.C., Esparta conquistó un área vecina y esclavizó a sus habitantes, quienes se denominaron ilotas. El temor a las revueltas de los ilotas hizo que Esparta se centrara en construir un ejército fuerte. El gobierno de Esparta era en parte una monarquía, en parte una oligarquía y en parte una democracia.

A la edad de siete años, los niños espartanos se mudaban a las viviendas militares llamadas barracas y comenzaban a recibir entrenamiento militar. Los hombres entraban al ejército a la edad de 20 años y servían hasta los 60. La educación para las niñas se enfocaba en lograr que fueran físicamente fuertes. Las mujeres espartanas tenían más libertad que en otras ciudades estado.

2. ¿Cómo se educaba a los niños espartanos?

_____

SECCIÓN 4: ESPARTA Y ATENAS, *CONTINUACIÓN*

La vida democrática de Atenas

A medida que Atenas se convertía en una democracia, su pueblo se centraba en los asuntos gubernamentales. Los atenienses estaban divididos en cuatro clases principales: ciudadanos, mujeres, personas libres que no eran ciudadanos y personas esclavizadas. Las personas esclavizadas constituían hasta un tercio de la población.

Los niños de las familias ricas comenzaban la escuela a la edad de seis o siete años. Su educación estaba diseñada para convertirlos en buenos ciudadanos. Las niñas no asistían a la escuela, pero aprendían de sus madres las tareas domésticas. Las mujeres atenienses eran respetadas por su rol de esposas y madres, pero tenían menos libertad que las mujeres espartanas.

3. ¿Cuál era el objetivo de la educación de los niños atenienses?

_____

_____

Las guerras persas

En el año 490 a.C. llegó a Grecia un ejército persa. Los persas querían castigar a los atenienses por haber ayudado a los griegos a rebelarse en Anatolia contra el dominio persa. En la llanura de Maratón, cerca de Atenas, los griegos derrotaron a los persas. La leyenda dice que un soldado corrió 25 millas desde Maratón hasta Atenas para anunciar la victoria. Las maratones actuales llevan ese nombre por este evento.

En el año 480 a.C., Persia invadió Grecia nuevamente. Varias ciudades estado se unieron en contra de Persia. Un ejército de 300 espartanos murieron en el estrecho pasaje ubicado en Termópilas para evitar que los persas llegaran a Atenas. Posteriormente, los atenienses derrotaron a los persas durante una batalla naval.

4. ¿Por qué los espartanos murieron en Termópilas?

_____

_____

 De cerca

Source: *Combat scene, a wounded or dead hoplite lies on the ground* (560–550 B.C.), Cleimachos. Pottery. Louvre, Paris. Photo © Erich Lessing/Art Resource, New York.

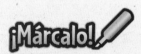 ¡Márcalo!

5. **Escribe un calce** que describa una batalla entre los griegos y los persas.

_____

_____

_____

CHAPTER
7 | BUILDING BACKGROUND VOCABULARY
Ancient Greece

A. Matching

Match the term with the best description. Write the letter of the term in the space provided.

_____ **1.** main part of a country or territory

_____ **2.** established; brought into being

_____ **3.** broke down or ended suddenly

_____ **4.** greatest in power or authority

_____ **5.** person who is loyal to and protected by a state or nation

_____ **6.** to have rights and privileges

_____ **7.** people who are in charge of a unit or group

_____ **8.** suggested, or put forward for consideration

a. citizen
b. collapsed
c. entitled
d. founded
e. mainland
f. proposed
g. supreme
h. supervisors

B. Synonyms and Antonyms

Write one synonym and one antonym for each boldfaced term.

9. rugged _____ _____

10. vivid _____ _____

11. gradual _____ _____

12. clever _____ _____

CHAPTER 7

A. Vocabulary Each of the questions below can be answered with a name or term from Chapter 7.

1. The Greeks believed that I was the ruler of the gods. Who am I?

   _____

2. I was the member of a group who had to work on the Spartans' farms.

   Who am I? _____

3. I was a free-born male who had the right to vote on laws. What am I?

   _____

4. I was a member of the trading people who taught the Greeks the alphabet.

   Who am I? _____

5. I was a Greek ruler who seized power by force. What am I?

   _____

B. Study Guide Write the terms, names, or phrases that best complete the sentences.

6. _____ focused all its efforts on building a strong military.

7. The southern part of the Greek peninsula is called the _____.

8. _____ was the place where the major Greek gods were

   supposed to live.

9. The city-state of _____ developed an early form of direct

   democracy.

10. _____ is rule by a king or queen who has supreme power.

11. The term _____ means "rule by the few."

12. The ancient _____ were athletic games held during a festival

   to honor Zeus.

13. The _____ is a system of symbols that stand for sounds.

14. Spartan soldiers went to live in military housing called _____.

15. Greece was divided into city-states. The Greek word for a city-state was

   _____.

CHAPTER 7 | SKILLBUILDER PRACTICE
Ancient Greece

Evaluating Information

To evaluate means to make a judgment about something. Historians evaluate information they learn about people, cultures, and events. They do this by deciding such things as what is the most important information, what caused an event to happen, and what are the positive and negative results of an event. Historians base their evaluations on research.

As you read the passage below, determine what the main point is and evaluate the information that is essential to the main point. (See Skillbuilder Handbook, page R14.)

The Greeks lived near several seas and designed boats to travel around the coasts and to other islands. They used square sails on their fishing boats and trading boats. Two or three sails were common. Trading ships had very deep hulls which helped them store a lot of cargo. Their fighting ships were called triremes. They were built for speed and mobility. About 150-170 oarsmen powered a trireme, but they also used sails. A trireme had three tiers of oars and sat low in the water. They were not made to go on long ocean voyages.

QUESTIONS

1. What is the main idea of this paragraph?

_____

_____

2. What statements convey information relevant to the main point?

_____

_____

3. Why do you think triremes were not good for long voyages?

_____

_____

CHAPTER

7 | HISTORY MAKERS
Homer

Epic Poet of Ancient Greece

Homer wrote two of the world's greatest epic poems, the Iliad *and the* Odyssey. *Yet the details of Homer's life are almost entirely unknown.*

Source: The Granger Collection, New York

Homer was a Greek poet who probably lived around 850 B.C. He may have been a wandering bard— someone who recited poems. According to tradition, he was blind, although this may be a myth. Homer may also have written some shorter poems called the Homeric Hymns. These poems praise gods worshipped during Homer's time.

Written over 2,000 years ago, Homer's poems have stood the test of time. No study of the world's great literature would be complete without the *Iliad* and the *Odyssey*. Both are epic poems—lengthy poems that tell of heroes and heroic actions.

The Iliad The *Iliad* takes place during the Trojan War, a struggle between the Greeks and Trojans. The war began after Paris, the son of Troy's king, fell in love with Helen, wife of the Greek king Menelaus, and carried Helen off to Troy. Menelaus swore vengeance. Through alliances, he assembled a force of 1,000 ships and 100,000 men. For this reason, Helen later became known as "the face that launched a thousand ships." The action of the *Iliad* takes place after Troy has been under siege for ten years. (In a siege, an army surrounds a city and tries to force it to surrender.) The poem focuses on Achilles, the strongest Greek warrior. But

it paints vivid portraits of many Greek and Trojan heroes and their deeds.

One of the most famous incidents of the Trojan War involves the Trojan Horse. Homer describes the story briefly in the *Odyssey*. This huge wooden horse housed 100 Greek warriors. After leaving the horse outside the gates of Troy, the rest of the Greek warriors boarded their ships and sailed out of the harbor. But they did not set sail for home. Instead, they hid close by. The Trojans thought the horse was a peace offering and took it into the city. That night, when the Trojans went to sleep, the Greek soldiers climbed out of the horse. They opened the gates to the rest of the Greek army, which entered the city and finally defeated the Trojans. The saying "beware of Greeks bearing gifts" refers to this story.

The Odyssey The hero of the *Odyssey* is Odysseus, who also is one of the Greek heroes of the *Iliad*. In the *Odyssey*, Odysseus and his men have many adventures on their return from the Trojan War. They fight a one-eyed giant. They encounter the Keeper of the Winds, who gives them a bag filled with favorable winds. An enchantress changes all but Odysseus into pigs—and then changes them back again. They visit Hades, the place of the dead. After a hurricane destroys his ship and crew, Odysseus is held captive for seven years. And when he finally returns home, he finds that his troubles are not yet over! Greedy men had invaded his home and tried to claim his wife and his property. Today we still use the word *odyssey* to describe a wandering or quest, often one with many adventures.

The Importance of Epic Poems Homer's poems were part of an oral tradition. Before written language was developed, bards sang or recited poems and stories. Epic poems were long, so bards often used stock phrases, which helped them memorize the poems. For example, Achilles is often described

CHAPTER 7

as "swift-footed Achilles." The bards also repeated parts of the poem as a refrain. This technique is still used in many modern poems and popular songs.

In ancient Athens, learning the *Iliad* and the *Odyssey* was an important part of a schoolboy's education. Students wrote out and memorized various passages. They often acted out scenes. They discussed the poems' heroes and why they acted the way they did.

The *Iliad* and the *Odyssey* may have been told and retold for several hundred years before being written down. This may explain why some dialects, or ways of speaking, used in the poems come from different time periods. Some scholars believe that more than one person may have created the poems.

The Trojan War Scholars believe that the Greeks's of Homer's time accepted his poems as history. While much of the *Odyssey* is too fantastic to be based on real events, the *Iliad* appears to be at least partly historic. The city of Troy actually existed and was located in northeastern Asia Minor.

For centuries, historians thought Troy was a product of Homer's imagination. But a German named Heinrich Schliemann disagreed. He was convinced that Troy had existed at one time. In 1870, he searched for and discovered the ancient city in what is now Turkey. He also found that Troy had been built on even older cities. Archaeologists eventually discovered that nine cities had been built on the site. Troy was somewhere in the middle.

The Trojan War also appears to have had a historic basis, although its cause was probably not the kidnapping of a queen. Instead, historians speculate that the war may have been caused by conflict over control of trade routes.

Homer's Influence Homer's poems have influenced other writers for centuries. The Roman poet Virgil used the *Odyssey* as the basis for his epic poem the *Aeneid*. His hero, Aeneas, was inspired by Odysseus. The

Aeneid glorified Roman values and became the national epic of Rome.

Major works of poetry and fiction have borrowed elements from the *Iliad* and the *Odyssey*. These include the novels *Don Quixote* by the Spanish writer Miguel de Cervantes and *Ulysses* (another name for Odysseus) by Irish writer James Joyce. The Italian Renaissance poet Dante was indirectly influenced by Homer through the works of other writers. Recently, the *Odyssey* was modernized in the film *O Brother, Where Art Thou,* and the Trojan War was the subject of the movie *Troy.*

CRITICAL THINKING QUESTIONS

1. **Find Main Ideas** Where and when does the *Iliad* take place?

2. **Synthesize** How does the *Odyssey* continue the story of the *Iliad?*

3. **Summarize** What is an epic poem?

4. **Categorize** What are some characteristics of Homer's epic poems?

5. **Make Inferences** Why were Homer's poems part of a schoolboy's education in ancient Greece?

6. **Recognize Changing Interpretations of History** Once scholars believed that neither the *Iliad* nor the *Odyssey* had any basis in fact. What caused them to change their minds about the *Iliad?*

CHAPTER
7 | CONNECT GEOGRAPHY & HISTORY
Ancient Greece

Mycenaean Greece

In about 2000 B.C., a Greek-speaking people moved from the north onto the Greek peninsula. These people built towns that were protected by strong walls. The larger cities had palaces. Each one was ruled by a king. Each king commanded a force of warriors who made up the noble class of the society.

The strongest of these fortified cities was called Mycenae. It was located on the Peloponnesus, the southern peninsula of Greece. Because of this city, the civilization developed by these earliest Greeks is called Mycenaean.

The Mycenaean Greeks were traders. Their society also had many fine artisans who could work with gold, silver, and bronze to make weapons and beautiful objects. Sometime around 1200 B.C., most of the Mycenaean cities were destroyed, perhaps by invaders. Civilization did not return to Greece for several hundred years.

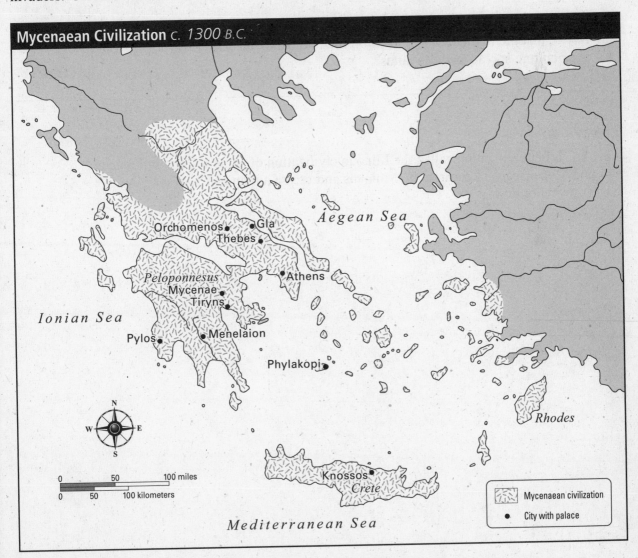

Mycenaean Civilization c. *1300 B.C.*

CONNECT GEOGRAPHY & HISTORY, *CONTINUED*

PRACTICE

Use the map to do these activities and answer the questions.

1. By what geographic feature are most of the Mycenaean cities located?

   _____

2. Judging from the location of the cities, which sea did the Mycenaeans sail on most often?

   _____

3. Draw a line from Mycenae to each of the other major cities shown on this map.

4. How would you describe the location of Mycenae compared to the other major cities?

   _____

5. Notice that the Mycenaean civilization includes some islands. How do you think their culture spread to those lands?

   _____

APPLY

6. An earlier civilization called the Minoan civilization of ancient Crete influenced the Mycenaeans. Research the Minoans and create a map of Crete showing their major cities.

CHAPTER
7 | OUTLINE MAP ACTIVITY
Ancient Greece

The Persian Wars *490–479* B.C.

A. Label the Map Use the map on textbook page 200 to locate the
following physical features, political features, and historical battles.
Then label them on the outline map on the back of this page. Also, title
your map and fill in the legend with the appropriate information.

Physical Features	Political Features	Historical Battles
Anatolia	Athens	Marathon (490 B.C.)
Aegean Sea	Sardis	Mycale (479 B.C.)
Mediterranean Sea	Sparta	Salamis (480 B.C.)
Naxos	Troy	Thermopylae (480 B.C.)
Rhodes	Greece	
	Persian Empire	

B. Questions After labeling your map, use it to answer the following
questions.

1. Where did the first battle occur?

_____

2. How far would troops leaving Sardis have
to travel over land to reach Thermopylae?

3. Which city is further north: Athens or
Sardis?

_____

4. How many Persian victories are
represented on the map?

_____

5. How far is it from Marathon to Athens?

6. Why would the side with a superior navy
have an advantage in this region?

_____

7. How long did the wars last?

_____

8. What advantage did Greece have at the
battles of Thermopylae, Salamis, and
Marathon?

_____

9. How many rivers would an army traveling
over land from Sardis to Greece have to
cross?

_____

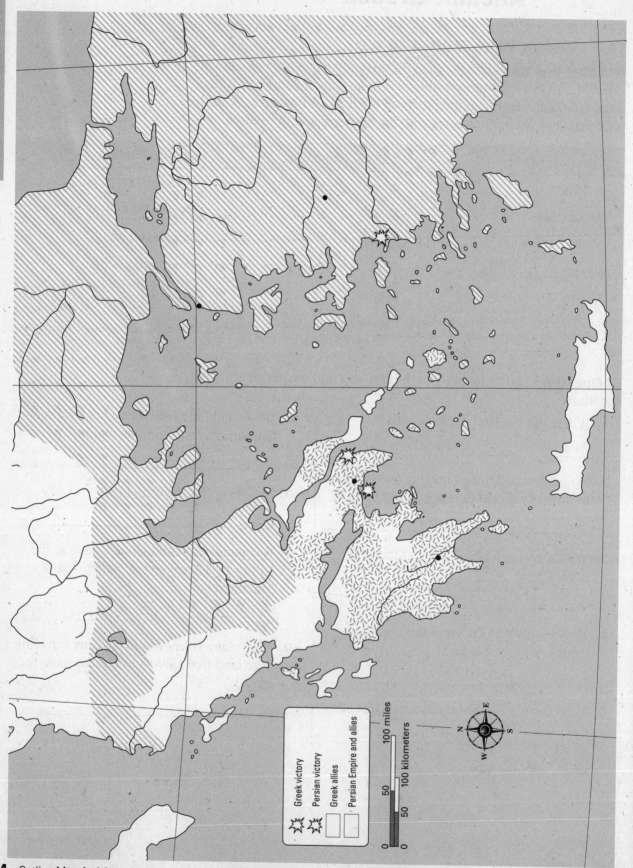

Greek victory

Persian victory

Greek allies

Persian Empire and allies

100 miles

100 kilometers

50

50

0

0

PRIMARY AND SECONDARY SOURCES
Ancient Greece

Poem by Solon

Solon was born into a well-to-do family of Athens and worked as a merchant. Solon entertained himself with poetry. He also used poetry to convey his ideas to the Athenians. He did not highly regard money, as is evident from his poems. The following poem by Solon was written around 590 B.C.

Athens' own people, for the sake of money, are determined to ruin this great city by their foolishness. The leaders of the common people have an unjust mind. They are bound to suffer terribly because of their outrageous behavior. For they do not know how to restrain excess or to behave properly when people are having a good time at a feast. . . .

They grow wealthy because they put their trust in unjust deeds.

They steal right and left with no respect for possessions sacred or profane. They have no respect for the awesome foundations of Justice, who is perfectly aware in her silence of what is and what has been, and who someday comes to pay back injustices.

This is a wound that inevitably comes to every city. And when it comes, the city falls into slavery. And that rouses strife and awakens slumbering war, which destroys the lovely prime of so many men. The meetings which the unrighteous love quickly destroy a fine city through the acts of the people who hate her.

These are the kind of terrible things that are occurring among the plain people. Many of the poor are being sent off to foreign lands as slaves. And there, in shameful chains they are forced to do the work of slaves.

Wrongs like this are forcing their way into every house. Doors don't lock calamity out. It jumps the wall and finds a man even if he locks himself in his bedroom.

This is what my heart tells me to tell the people of Athens: that just as bad government produces trouble for a city, good government makes things orderly and right, and it often chains up the unjust. Good government makes the rough smooth. It stops excess. It stymies outrageous behavior. It kills the weeds of ruin even as they grow. It corrects corrupt judgments. It tames arrogant behavior. It puts a stop to rebellions and to the bitterness of destructive strife. Good government makes things appropriate and right in human affairs.

Poems of Solon, Poem 4, ca. 590 B.C.

DOCUMENT–BASED QUESTIONS

1. **Summarize** According to Solon, how will Athenians ruin their city?

   _____

   _____

2. **Find Main Ideas** Above all else, what is the cure for the city in danger of ruin due to corruptness?

   _____

   _____

3. **Form and Support Opinions** Which do you think Solon views as a bigger wound to the city, theft or slavery? Why?

   _____

   _____

4. **Make Inferences** What is Solon trying to convince his fellow citizens to do or embrace?

   _____

   _____

CHAPTER 7

CHAPTER 7 | LITERATURE
Ancient Greece

The Odyssey by Homer

After the Trojan War, Odysseus and the other Greeks set sail to return to their kingdoms. Early in their voyage, Odysseus and his men were captured by a one-eyed giant who ate some of the men and planned to eat them all. Odysseus tricked the giant and blinded his eye, which allowed Odysseus and his crew to escape. However, the giant was the son of the sea god, Poseidon, who took revenge on Odysseus by keeping him from reaching home. *The Odyssey* tells the story of this journey. This translation uses the Roman names for the Greek characters: Odysseus is referred to as Ulysses, Zeus is Jove, Poseidon is Neptune, and Athena is called Minerva.

And Jove said, . . . "How can I forget Ulysses than whom there is no more capable man on earth, nor more liberal in his offerings to the immortal gods that live in heaven? Bear in mind, however, that Neptune is still furious with Ulysses for having blinded an eye of Polyphemus king of the Cyclopes. Polyphemus is son to Neptune by the nymph Thoosa, daughter to the sea-king Phorcys; therefore though he will not kill Ulysses outright, he torments him by preventing him from getting home. Still, let us lay our heads together and see how we can help him to return; Neptune will then be pacified, for if we are all of a mind he can hardly stand out against us."

And Minerva said, . . . "Father, if, then, the gods now mean that Ulysses should get home, . . . I will go to Ithaca, to put heart into Ulysses' son Telemachus; I will embolden him to call the Achaeans in assembly, and speak out to the suitors of his mother Penelope, who persist in eating up any number of his sheep and oxen; I will also conduct him to Sparta and to Pylos, to see if he can hear anything about the return of his dear father—for this will make people speak well of him."

from *The Odyssey*, Book I, Homer, trans. Samuel Butler

CRITICAL THINKING

1. **Find Main Ideas** Why and how does Neptune (Poseidon) torment Ulysses (Odysseus)?

_____

2. **Draw Conclusions** What characteristic of Greek gods does this passage show?

_____

3. **Make Inferences** What does Minerva (Athena) mean when she says "I will go to Ithaca, to put heart into Ulysses' son Telemachus"?

_____

Atalanta's Last Race

Background: According to Greek myth, the father of Atalanta (AT•uh•LAN•tuh) wanted a son, not a daughter. So he left Atalanta to die in the wilderness as an infant. She was raised first by a mother bear and then by caring hunters. As a result, the beautiful young woman was skilled in running, hunting, and wrestling.

Cast of Characters
Narrator
Oeneus: (EE•yoost) king of Calydon
Atalanta: a young Greek woman
Hunter: Atalanta's foster father
Meleager: (mehl•ee•AY•guhr) son of Oeneus
Iasus: (EYE•ah•suhs) father of Atalanta
Aphrodite: (AF•ruh•DY•tee) Greek goddess of love
Milanion: (my•LAN•ee•uhn) suitor of Atalanta
Spectator

The Atalanta Lekythos (Funerary Oil Jug) (500–490 B.C.), attributed to Douris. Greek. Photo © The Cleveland Museum of Art

Atalanta Running This vase from about 500 B.C. depicts the myth of Atalanta running in her famous race.

Narrator: The goddess Artemis (AHR•tuh•mihs) is angry at King Oeneus because he forgot to make sacrifices to her. So she has sent a wild boar to destroy his country of Calydon (KAL•ih•DAHN). The king has asked the best hunters in Greece for help. When they arrive, Atalanta is with them. She stands before the king, looking lovely in her simple woolen robe. A quiver of arrows hangs over her left shoulder. Her right hand clasps her bow.

Oeneus: Who are you, young woman? I have need of skilled hunters, not foolish girls.

Atalanta: Your majesty, I think you will find that I am as skilled as any man here. I have spent my life in the woods.

Hunter: I can speak for her, my lord. Atalanta has lived among us since she was a small girl. She once killed two centaurs [creatures that were half-man, half horse] singlehandedly. In our land, she is known as "the pride of the woods."

CHAPTER 7

Oeneus: Very well, let us see what she can do. We need all the help we can get.

Narrator: The king's son Meleager falls in love with Atalanta instantly. Although some of the men dislike the idea of hunting with a woman, Meleager insists that she go with them.

Meleager: Come, Atalanta, you can hunt by my side. If you are as skilled as the hunters say, I will be glad of your presence. In fact, I should like you always near me.

Atalanta: I am happy to be your friend, Meleager, and I look forward to the hunt. But I only care for men as fellow hunters. I don't plan to ever get married.

Narrator: When the hunters surround the boar, it attacks and kills two men. Atalanta stays calm, and it is her arrow that first strikes the animal. Meleager then moves in for the kill.

Source: The Granger Collection, New York

Artemis The goddess Artemis, sister of Apollo, was another female in Greek mythology who was a skilled hunter.

Meleager: Although it is my knife that has killed this beast, I insist that the honor go to Atalanta. She shall have the boar skin as a trophy.

Narrator: Meleager's uncles quarrel with him because he honored Atalanta. This quarrel leads to his death. But Atalanta's fame is just beginning. After defeating a great hero in a wrestling match, she meets her father, Iasus.

Iasus: Congratulations, daughter. I am very proud of you and would like to welcome you back to my home. I see that you will be almost like a son to me. But I understand that many young men want to marry you.

Atalanta: Don't worry, Father, I will never marry a man unless he can beat me in a foot race. *[Aside]* And I know there is no man alive who can do that.

Narrator: Atalanta enjoys defeating all the young men who come to race with her. No matter how fast they are, she is faster. She cares nothing for their promises of love. Her actions do not go unnoticed by Aphrodite, the goddess of love on Mount Olympus.

Aphrodite It has come to my attention that there is a wild young maiden who thinks she is too good for love. I may need to teach her a lesson.

Narrator: As it happens, a young man named Milanion wants very much to marry Atalanta. He is smart enough to know he cannot rely on his speed to beat her. He calls upon Aphrodite.

Milanion: Aphrodite, will you help me to gain the love of Atalanta?

Source: © CM Dixon/Heritage-Images

Running Girl In Sparta, girls were trained in athletics because it taught them to be strong. Also, every four years at a festival in Hera's honor, unmarried girls competed in races.

CHAPTER 7

Aphrodite: I will gladly help tame this young woman who refuses to honor me. Here are three magical golden apples. Their beauty is so dazzling that anyone who sees them will feel she must have them. Use them wisely and you will succeed.

Milanion: Thank you, goddess, for your wise and generous assistance.

Narrator: The day arrives when Milanion and Atalanta are to race. Atalanta looks so confident of her skill that Milanion almost despairs of being able to succeed in his plan.

Milanion: I must not lose courage. Aphrodite is on my side.

Narrator: The race begins. Milanion is swift, but Atalanta is pulling ahead. He rolls his first golden apple right in front of her.

Atalanta: Oh my! What is this? I've never seen anything so lovely. I'll just reach down and scoop it up.

Milanion: She barely lost her stride! I've caught up with her, but now she is racing ahead again. I've got to slow her down even more.

Narrator: This time, Milanion throws his apple to Atalanta's side. She has to move to the right to pick it up.

Spectator: Look, he's pulled ahead of her! But here she comes again, and the finish line is just ahead. Will she win this time?

Milanion: This is my last chance. I must distract her long enough for me to reach the goal ahead of her. Here goes.

Narrator: The third golden apple rolls right in front of Atalanta and onto the side of the racecourse. She sees it glinting in the green grass and follows it.

Atalanta: I must have that gorgeous glowing ball. But wait, what's this? Milanion is sprinting past me. He has won!

Milanion: *[panting for breath]* Atalanta, do not be angry with me. I only acted out of my great love for you. I will be extremely honored to be your husband.

Atalanta: I admire your skill and your wit. And I see that Aphrodite is your friend. I will honor my promise and be your wife.

Activities

1. **Talk About It** Why might Atalanta prefer not to marry?

2. **Write About It** Imagine that you are a spectator watching the race between Atalanta and Milanion. Write a paragraph describing the details of the race—the sights, the sounds, and other important impressions.

INTERDISCIPLINARY PROJECT

Greek Numbers

As all students do today, ancient Greek boys studied arithmetic. However, they used a number system very different from the one we use. The Greek number system was alphabetical. The number symbols were the same as the letters of the Greek alphabet. Nine letters were needed for the units, nine for the tens, and nine for the hundreds. In total that is 27 letters. Because the Greek alphabet had only 24 letters, three additional characters

were added. The digamma for 6, the koppa for 90, and the sampi for 900. The list of Greek numbers is shown below.

To write a number that combined numbers listed in the chart, Greeks wrote the largest number first. For example, $\Phi\Pi A = 581$

The Greeks indicated thousands (1,000 to 9,000) by placing an apostrophe before a unit. For example, $'E\Phi\Pi A = 5581$

Alpha	Beta	Gamma	Delta	Epsilon	Digamma	Zeta	Eta	Theta
A	B	Γ	Δ	E	F	Z	H	θ
1	2	3	4	5	6	7	8	9

Iota	Kappa	Lamda	Mu	Nu	Xi	Omicron	Pi	Koppa
I	K	Λ	M	N	Ξ	O	Π	Ϙ
10	20	30	40	50	60	70	80	90

Rho	Sigma	Tau	Upsilon	Phi	Chi	Psi	Omega	Sampi
P	Σ	T	Y	Φ	X	Ψ	Ω	⩚
100	200	300	400	500	600	700	800	900

Project

Create an arithmetic worksheet using Greek numbers.

1 Trade worksheets with a classmate.

2 Solve the problems on the worksheet you received.

3 Together, check the answers to both worksheets.

QUESTIONS

1. Write the Greek number for 6,287.

2. What number is equal to the Greek number $P N$?

3. What is the major difference between the ancient Greek number system and the number system you use to calculate?

CHAPTER 7 | INTERDISCIPLINARY PROJECT

Drying Food for Trade

7B Connect to Science

Nearly all parts of Greece lie within 100 miles of the sea. Most ancient Greek cities had a port. The ancient Greeks used the sea to travel between their own cities and to the world beyond to trade goods. One of the products they had plenty to trade was fish. The Greeks traveled up the coast and traded fresh fish to local ports. However, fresh fish does not stay fresh very long. To transport fish long distances, they had to find a way to prevent the fish from spoiling quickly. To accomplish this, the Greeks dried fish and other foods. Dried foods do not spoil as quickly as fresh foods. The Greeks used the sun to dehydrate, or remove most of the water from, food. Greek climate with its dry air, clear skies, and steady breezes is perfect for drying foods. Modern people still use the sun to dehydrate some foods. The process has not changed much for thousands of years.

Project

Model the drying process used by the ancient Greeks to preserve food.

1. Slice two thoroughly-washed Roma tomatoes in half. **CAUTION:** Follow safety guidelines for using a sharp knife.

2. Weigh each half. Measure the length, width, and thickness of each half. Record all of your data.

3. Place slices cut side up on a clean piece of raised screening or a drying tray.

4. Sprinkle the tomatoes lightly with sea salt.

5. Cover the tomatoes with a tent made of cheesecloth. Do not let the cheesecloth touch the tomatoes.

6. Place the tray in the sun to dry. If you set the tray outdoors, you must bring it in at night and when it rains. It will take between 4 and 14 days for the tomatoes to dry.

7. When the tomatoes are dry, weigh and measure them as you did in Step 1. Record your data.

MATERIALS
• 2 tomatoes
• kitchen knife
• food scale
• ruler or tape measure
• pencil and paper
• drying tray
• sea salt
• cheesecloth

QUESTIONS

1. How much did drying change the weight of the tomatoes?

2. How much did drying change the size of the tomatoes?

3. How would drying foods benefit traders?

4. Do you think sun drying would be practical in a very humid climate? Why or why not?

CHAPTER
7 | INTERDISCIPLINARY PROJECT
Aesop's Fables

7C Connect to
Language Arts

A fable is story that teaches a lesson. Although the moral is sometimes stated at the end of the story, the lesson is usually clear from the story alone. A Greek man named Aesop (EE•sop), who lived in the 500s B.C., is credited with making up the most famous fables in the world. Among some of the most well-known tales are "The Tortoise and the Hare" and "The Lion and the Mouse." Most of the time, the characters in the stories are animals instead of people. The fables have been translated into many languages and are still being retold today. Below is another well-known Aesop's fable, "The Ant and the Grasshopper." What do you think of the moral of this story? Do you agree or disagree? Are you more like the ant or the grasshopper?

The Ant and the Grasshopper

One beautiful, hot summer day, Grasshopper was happily hopping about in a field, singing and playing. He hadn't a care in the world. Just then, Ant passed by. On his sturdy back he carried a huge kernel of corn. He was struggling to get it back to his nest.

"Oh, come and play with me!" cried Grasshopper. "It's too pretty today to toil away like that."

For a minute, Ant put down his burden. "I am helping to store food for the winter," said Ant. "I don't have time to play all day. And if I were you, I'd be doing the same!"

"Oh, I'm not worried," Grasshopper replied. "Look at all the food in this field! How could I ever go hungry? I'm not going to waste such a nice day worrying about the future." Ant just shook his head, picked up his corn, and went on his way.

Many more times Ant passed Grasshopper. Each time Grasshopper was singing a carefree tune in the sun as Ant struggled past. Grasshopper was having too much fun to work as hard as Ant.

Eventually winter came. Then Grasshopper had no food. He got hungrier and hungrier. The ants, he knew, were snug in their tunnels. They were munching the food they had worked so hard to save during the summer. As he weakly hopped to the anthill to beg for food, he realized:

It is a good idea to put something aside in the good times so you will be prepared for the bad times.

Project

Write your own fable.

1 Visit the library or use Internet sources to read several other examples of Aesop's fables.

2 Think about a life lesson you have learned or think is important.

3 Then write a fable that illustrates your lesson in the style of one of Aesop's fables. Be sure the moral of your story is clear, whether or not you state it at the end.

4 Share your fable with your classmates.

CHAPTER **7** | INTERDISCIPLINARY PROJECT
The Olympics

7D Connect to
Physical Education

Did you know that the Olympic games are ancient, not modern? They were first held in 776 B.C. By the 500s B.C., the Olympic games were one of the major events in the classical Greek world. Like all Greek games, the Olympics were part of a major religious celebration. They were held to honor Zeus, king of the gods. Every four years—a period of time called an Olympiad—athletes flocked to the town of Olympia. Only free Greek men could take part, although games for boys were later added. Aside from one priestess, women could not attend the games. If they were caught sneaking in, they were put to death.

The ancient Olympics included boxing and wrestling matches, foot races, chariot races, and the pentathlon—a collection of five track and field events. The winners were given wreaths or garlands made of olive branches. In addition, these men became superstars. They brought honor and fame to themselves and to their hometowns. They were also given very special treatment.

The Olympics died out during Roman times. The later Romans did not really approve of athletic games of this style. However, about 2,000 years later, a French baron named Pierre de Coubertin (kooh•bear•TAHN) dreamed of starting the games again. Due to his efforts, the first modern Olympics were held in Greece in 1896. In 1924, the Winter Games were added. Today, athletes from around the world compete in events with roots in ancient Greece.

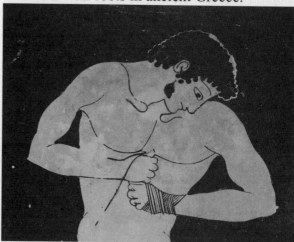

Source: A boxer bandaging his wrist before the fight (5th century B.C.), Greek. Detail of red-figured amphora. Inv. 3723. Kunsthistorisches Museum, Vienna, Austria. Photo © Erich Lessing/Art Resource, New York.

Project

Hold a pentathlon of your own.

1. The original events included a foot race, wrestling, long jump, discus, and javelin. Your pentathlon could include any individual sport or game—100-yard dash, arm wrestling, darts. Choose five competitions that test a wide range of abilities.

2. Form into teams of five students each.

3. Have volunteers act as officials to measure and record results.

4. Allow each athlete two tries and record his or her best effort. For races, hold a trial run before the actual race.

5. After all events are completed, present medals or ribbons for first, second, and third places to winning individuals and teams.

TEAM TEACHING STRATEGIES
Ancient Greece

7A Connect to Math
Greek Numbers

7B Connect to Science
Drying Food for Trade

OBJECTIVES

- To analyze the Greek number system
- To convert Greek numbers to base-10 and to write the Greek equivalent for a given base-10 number
- To create an arithmetic worksheet to practice writing and decoding Greek numbers

STRATEGIES FOR THE MATH TEACHER

1. Distribute Project 7A to the class and have students read the material.
2. Test student understanding by converting a few examples on the chalkboard. Include examples of both reading and writing Greek numbers.
3. When students have prepared the worksheets, organize students in pairs to trade worksheets.
4. In case of disagreement, put the number in question on the chalkboard and discuss as a class.

ANSWERS

1. 6,287 = apostrophe, digamma, sigma, eta, zeta.
2. 150
3. Possible answers: The Greek number system does not use 0; the Greek number system uses many more symbols.

RUBRIC

Students should be able to

- write the base-10 equivalent for numbers written in the Greek number system
- write the Greek equivalent for numbers written in base-10
- create a worksheet to aid in reading and writing the Greek number system

OBJECTIVES

- To prepare and dry tomatoes in the sun
- To compare the effects of drying on the size and weight of tomatoes
- To infer the type of climate that would be suitable for drying food by using the sun

STRATEGIES FOR THE SCIENCE TEACHER

1. Prepare a place to dry the tomatoes. Dry directly outdoors only if you have a dry climate. Drying indoors in a sunny window can also work.
2. Distribute Project 7B to the class. Answer any questions.
3. Distribute materials to student groups. **CAUTION:** Review safe ways to handle a knife.

ANSWERS

1. Answers will vary.
2. Answers will vary.
3. Drying reduces size and weight, allowing traders to carry more on each trip.
4. No. The moisture would keep the food from drying properly.

RUBRIC

Students should be able to

- follow direction for drying tomatoes
- compare weight and size before and after drying
- conclude that climate can determine the practicality of sun drying food

CHAPTER 7

7C Connect to Language Arts
Aesop's Fables

OBJECTIVES

- To explore Greek fables
- To write a fable that illustrates a moral lesson

STRATEGIES FOR THE LANGUAGE ARTS TEACHER

1. Distribute Project 7C to the class. Give students a few minutes to read the material. Discuss with students what the purpose of a fable might be. Ask: Why would someone write fables? Students should understand that fables are a way to teach cultural ideas and values.

2. Have a volunteer read "The Ant and the Grasshopper" aloud. Then discuss with students the moral of the story and whether or not they agree with the moral.

3. Before writing, brainstorm with students a list of lessons it might be helpful for people to learn in life. Write their responses on the chalkboard.

4. Extend the activity by having volunteers read their fables aloud to the class. Ask students to summarize the moral lesson taught by each fable.

5. Alternatively, have students create illustrations and title pages for their fables. Bind the fables together to make a classroom book of fables.

RUBRIC

Students' fables should

- illustrate a moral lesson with animal characters
- contain vivid language and descriptions, with correct spelling and usage

7D Connect to Physical Education
The Olympics

OBJECTIVES

- To explore classical Greek athletics
- To identify the Olympics as an ancient sporting event that is also held today
- To hold and participate in a sporting event modeled on the Olympics

STRATEGIES FOR THE PHYSICAL EDUCATION TEACHER

1. Distribute Project 7D to the class. Give students time to read the material. Ask students what they know about the Olympics. Most students will be familiar with the Olympic games or well-known Olympic athletes.

2. Provide time for students to plan the pentathlon. Have them, with your input, consider if they want to hold one event on each day or hold all events on the same day. Determine which events students will participate in and make sure that each team includes students of varying abilities. If possible, have volunteers act as officials, instead of assigning these positions. Have students decide on and create the prizes.

3. Provide any necessary equipment. Allow time and space for students to practice and then run each event. Hold an award ceremony following the last event.

RUBRIC

Students should

- understand the roots of the Olympic games
- hold and participate in their own pentathlon

BRINGING SOCIAL STUDIES ALIVE

Research a Greek God

Greek gods played an important part in the lives of Greek citizens. The gods were responsible for nature and human conditions. Citizens made offerings to specific gods who controlled specific areas.

MATERIALS
• books on Greek gods
• Internet access

Week 1: Choose a God to Research (30 minutes) Divide the class into groups of four. Let each group meet to choose a god or goddess to research. Each group should turn in the name to the teacher, who can make sure there are no duplicates. Let the groups choose from a list of the following gods and goddesses:

Zeus, supreme god
Aphrodite, goddess of love and beauty
Apollo, god of prophesy, music, and healing
Ares, god of war
Artemis, goddess of the hunt
Athena, goddess of crafts and domestic arts
Demeter, goddess of agriculture
Dionysus, god of wine and the theater
Hephaestus, god of fire
Hera, goddess of marriage
Hermes, messenger and guide of dead souls
Poseidon, god of the sea

Each group will research and write a short paper about their chosen deity. The paper should include a bibliography. Things the group will want to research include the history of the god or goddess, important relatives, powers, dealings with humans in myths, official symbols linked to the god or goddess.

Week 2: Research at the Media Center (45 minutes) Ask the media specialist to have books pulled that deal with Greek mythology. Each group should assign each of its members a section to research for the deity. Encourage the students to read from books before going to an encyclopedia or the Internet, but those sources may also be used. Have each student responsible for a different bibliographical entry. Mention that similar information may be found in different sources. This is how students can factcheck the material to make sure it is correct. When a student finds information that belongs in another student's section of the report, he or she should share that information with the other student.

Week 3: Compile the Paper (45 minutes) Have the group members write up one final report combining their research.

Week 4: Present Information to the Class (45 minutes) Each group will present its paper to the class with individual members presenting the information for his or her section. Encourage students to use props and illustrations to enhance their presentations.

CHAPTER

7

BRINGING SOCIAL STUDIES ALIVE

The Mountainous Regions

Geography
Activity

About 80 percent of Greece is mountainous, which leaves little land for agriculture. The long coastline around the peninsulas and the many islands that are part of Greece encouraged boat building, exploration, colonization, and trade. By coloring a topographical map of Greece, you can understand how isolated the city-states were. You can also understand why the sea played such an important part in the development of Greek society.

MATERIALS
• outline map of Greece
• colored pencils
• topographical map of Greece

A LAND OF MOUNTAINS

1. Refer to the topographical map of Greece and lightly draw in the areas that are mountainous.
2. Color in the mountainous areas on your map with a brown pencil.
3. With a green pencil, color the areas around the coasts.
4. Label the bodies of water surrounding the Greek peninsula. Lightly color the water blue.
5. Draw stars for the locations of Athens and Sparta and label them.
6. Write three questions that can be answered by using your map. Trade questions with another student. Answer each other's questions.

CHAPTER

7 | BRINGING SOCIAL STUDIES ALIVE
Greek Coins

Hands-On Activity

Through trade, Greeks were introduced to coins. Many coins showed a likeness of a god or goddess and a symbol of something that was important to that particular deity. Look at the coin shown on page 181 of your textbook. You can design your own coin.

MATERIALS
• self-hardening clay
• pencil or sculpting tool

GETTING STARTED

1. Research a god or goddess by using books or the Internet. Find out what the god was supposed to have looked like and what symbols were associated with him.
2. Make sketches of the god or goddess and any symbols associated with him or her.
3. Roll two small balls of clay and flatten them into a circular shape.
4. Use your sketches to help you sculpt a profile of a god or goddess on one circle. On the other circle sculpt a symbol associated with that deity.
5. Carefully place the two blank sides of the clay circles together and pinch the edges together so that they form one coin.

CHECKLIST

❑ My coin has a likeness of a god or goddess on one side.
❑ My coin has a symbol of the god or goddess on the other side.

CHAPTER 7

BRINGING SOCIAL STUDIES ALIVE

Different Government Styles in Greece

Simulation Overview

In this simulation, students work with a group to develop laws for an imaginary city-state. Each city-state has a different style of government. Students will present the laws they develop to the whole class.

PROCEDURES

- Have students divide into five groups, which represent city-states. Each group will develop a different style of government. Assign one group to develop a monarchy. For this group, appoint a king. He will make laws and assign positions (slave, noble, etc.) to the other members of the group. Another group will be an aristocracy. Another will be oligarchy. For one group, appoint a tyrant. Be sure that group has students who represent the poor people who put the tyrant in power. The fifth group will be a direct democracy.

- Each group will develop a job or position for each member of the group.

- Each group will develop five laws. In the case of a monarchy or a tyrant, use the pattern of Sparta's government where there are elected assemblies.

- Give each group 30 minutes to develop 5 laws for its type of government.

- Have the highest-ranking person present the laws to the class and explain the type of government in that particular city-state.

CHAPTER 7 | BRINGING SOCIAL STUDIES ALIVE
A Day at the Agora

Performance Activity

Introduction

The agora was a place where farmers sold their produce, shopkeepers sold their wares, fish sellers sold fish, and political discussions were held. Let's listen in to some conversations at Athens' agora.

CAST OF CHARACTERS

Narrator

Fish seller

First foreign traveler

Second foreign traveler

Perry: a wealthy Greek

Theo: another wealthy Greek

Farmer

Shoemaker

First slave

Second slave

Milean: Greek factory owner

Lennious: Greek city official

Slave seller

Tomias: Greek banker

Narrator: It is the year 500 B.C. on a fine summer day in Athens. Here come two foreigners, from the looks of their hats. No one in Athens would wear traveling gear to the agora. Oh, listen, the fish seller is ringing his bell. Fish must have just been brought in.

Fish seller: Fish! Fresh fish!

First foreign traveler: Have you ever seen so many fish sellers? I wish that we could get this type of fish back home.

Second foreign traveler: Yes, the pickled stuff we eat isn't as kind to the tongue as this fine fresh catch. The fish we ate at noon was very tasty.

First foreign traveler: Do you think we could carry some home if we had a big jar with water in it?

Second foreign traveler: You mean keep the fish alive until we arrived home?

First foreign traveler: We could give it a try, but it would be awfully heavy, wouldn't it?

Second foreign traveler: I think two slaves could carry it between them if we found a jar with handles on both sides.

Narrator: The two foreigners stroll among the stalls looking for a Greek vessel that would house a fish or two on a journey of 50 miles into the mountains. Here are two friends who are visiting. Let's listen to them.

Perry: There was more talk about the Timmin trial. You would think the debate was not over and the votes cast. He deserved more than 10 years banishment from Athens, I think. But majority rules, of course.

Theo: Of course. Wonder where the fellow will go? Probably Sparta. He'd fit right in with his violent ways.

Perry: He's the type that would be so bold as to climb Mount Olympus. The gods would throw him out for sure.

Narrator: Let's walk this way among the stalls and see what's for sale.

Farmer: Olives! Olive oil! Fine jar of olive oil.

Narrator: It looks good. What else is here?

Farmer: I have some apples and pomegranates. Would you care for some of these?

Narrator: Just looking, thanks. The smell is rather strong here. Oh, its that cheese, I think. Potent stuff.

Farmer: It is tasty goat cheese, aged just right.

Narrator: I can smell that.

Slave seller: Slaves! Two young girls, trained in housework. Three boys ready for the fields or the factory. This woman would be good for lots of work.

Narrator: Where did you get the slaves?

Slave seller: These two girls were sold by their poor parents right here in Athens. Kidnappers brought these three boys and the young woman. They are probably from Thrace.

Narrator: Don't you feel slavery is wrong?

Slave seller: What's wrong about it? Everyone needs a slave or two. Why, I just sold three to a man who has at least five-hundred slaves. He rents them out to others for day labor. People who need someone to tell them what to do make the best slaves.

Narrator: Let's follow these two slaves. They are carrying something heavy between them. Hey there, what have you got?

First slave: We are carrying fish for our master.

Narrator: Would your master be the fellow over there in the fine purple robe?

Second slave: That would be him. We must hurry to keep up with him.

Narrator: How does it feel to be a slave?

First slave: How do you think it feels? It's hard labor, day in and day out. We don't have any choice. Just do as we're told. I hope to someday be set free, but I don't know that the day will come.

Second slave: Hurry, the master is turning to look for us.

Narrator: Well, here we are by the shoemaker's spot. He seems to be a fine craftsman.

Shoemaker: Are you looking for sandals?

Narrator: No, I'm just looking around. What's that over there where the men have gathered?

Shoemaker: That's the barbershop. Only one man is getting his hair cut. The others are just talking.

Narrator: We'll go eavesdrop a bit.

Milean: So will the Council meet tomorrow?

Lennious: Yes. We will talk about the candidates and see which ones are qualified to serve on the 500.

Tomias: I heard that someone had the nerve to claim he was a citizen when clearly he was not born in our fair city.

Lennious: You can never tell with some people. They cheat their way through life and lie.

Milean: I should take the fellow and put him to work in the factory. He would find there is no cheating his way if he worked near the fires, pounding on the metal to make the shields. I am so proud of my factory, but I wouldn't want to be one of the workers. Of course, most of them are slaves, so I guess it doesn't matter that the work is hot.

Narrator: Here come the fellows we saw earlier.

Perry: Tomias, I thought you were coming to the presentation last night. I was looking forward to hearing you discuss the case.

Tomias: I've said all I care to say about the Timmin trial. We won't hear from him again.

Lennious: We should ostracize this fellow I was talking about who lied about being a citizen.

Theo: I heard about him. What was his name? Neocles?

Lennious: That's the one, Neocles, son of Diocles. Or so he says.

Perry: You just can't trust everyone. I've got to go.

Theo: I'll walk with you. I should buy supplies for my presentation. It will be in two nights. We'll start at sundown. I hope you will all be able to come.

Tomias: Sorry, I'll be at the theater. I promised my brother that we could go.

CHAPTER 7

Theo: We'll miss you.

Narrator: Let's see what else is for sale. I smell perfume. This vendor has a unique blend for sale. I wonder if it will be successful.

Perfume salesman: You are a wise man to think this is a good scent. It is a new discovery. Brewed with the freshest herbs and with a hint of a secret ingredient.

Narrator: So, you think everyone will be wearing it soon?

Perfume salesman: It's the best. Want to try a little?

Narrator: I think I'll pass on that. Oh, listen the fish seller is ringing his bell. Another catch of fish must have arrived. See how everyone swarms over for the freshest fish. There go the two foreigners again. Those poor slaves will be carrying even more pots with fish swimming in them.

Perfume salesman: You sure you don't want perfume? It will make the smell of the fish not so bad.

Narrator: Thanks, I think I'll call it a day and make my way home.

SECTION 1

SECTION 1 QUIZ

The Geography of Greece

Multiple Choice
Choose the letter of the best answer.

_____ 1. A body of land with water on three sides is a(n)

    a. continent.

    b. island.

    c. isthmus.

    d. peninsula.

_____ 2. Greece is a peninsula that has a southern peninsula called

    a. Athens.

    b. Phoenicia.

    c. Peloponnesus.

    d. Sparta.

_____ 3. A narrow strip of land between two bodies of water is a(n)

    a. bridge.

    b. isthmus.

    c. peninsula.

    d. strait.

_____ 4. The Greeks used a system of writing developed by the

    a. Egyptians.

    b. Phoenicians.

    c. Mycenaeans.

    d. Romans.

_____ 5. A system of writing that uses symbols to stand for individual sounds is called a(n)

    a. alphabet.

    b. character.

    c. codex.

    d. hieroglyph.

_____ 6. The main products that the Greeks traded for were grain, timber, animal hides, and

    a. slaves.

    b. olive oil.

    c. wine.

    d. fine pottery.

_____ 7. The first Greek civilization was called

    a. Peloponnesian civilization.

    b. Mycenaean civilization.

    c. Phoenician civilization.

    d. Mediterranean civilization.

_____ 8. In Greece, mountains cover about

    a. 10 percent of the land.

    b. 25 percent of the land.

    c. 50 percent of the land.

    d. 75 percent of the land.

_____ 9. Because of their location, the ancient Greeks became skilled

    a. sailors.

    b. horse riders.

    c. road builders.

    d. foresters.

_____ 10. In order to get more farmland, the Greeks

    a. cleared forests.

    b. filled in river deltas.

    c. founded colonies in other regions.

    d. drained swamps.

SECTION

2

SECTION 2 QUIZ

Life in Ancient Greece

Multiple Choice

Choose the letter of the best answer.

_____ 1. The ruler of the Greek gods was called

    a. Ares.

    b. Athena.

    c. Prometheus.

    d. Zeus.

_____ 2. The Greeks believed the gods lived

    a. in Athens.

    b. in Cyprus.

    c. on Mount Olympus.

    d. on Mount Etna.

_____ 3. Stories that portray Greek gods and goddesses are called

    a. essays.

    b. fables.

    c. histories.

    d. myths.

_____ 4. The games held every four years at a festival to honor Zeus were called the

    a. Goodwill Games.

    b. marathons.

    c. Olympics.

    d. triathlons.

_____ 5. A short story, usually involving animals, that teaches a moral lesson is a(n)

    a. epic poem.

    b. fable.

    c. myth.

    d. song.

_____ 6. The *Iliad* is an example of a(n)

    a. epic poem.

    b. fable.

    c. novel.

    d. song.

_____ 7. According to Greek myth, Prometheus gave humans

    a. water.

    b. air.

    c. olives.

    d. fire.

_____ 8. The ancient Greeks honored their gods by

    a. holding festivals.

    b. going to church.

    c. raising money.

    d. having debating contests.

_____ 9. According to tradition, the *Iliad* and the *Odyssey* were composed by

    a. Aesop.

    b. Demeter.

    c. Homer.

    d. Zeus.

_____ 10. In "The Hare and the Tortoise," the hare loses the race because

    a. the tortoise tricks the hare.

    b. the hare takes a nap.

    c. the tortoise uses a magic spell.

    d. the hare gets lost.

SECTION

SECTION 3 QUIZ
The City-State and Democracy

3

Multiple Choice
Choose the letter of the best answer.

_____ **1.** In Greek, the word for city-state was

    a. civitas.

    b. barracks.

    c. democracy.

    d. polis.

_____ **2.** The upper class in Greece was called the

    a. aristocracy.

    b. monarchy.

    c. oligarchy.

    d. tyranny.

_____ **3.** A government ruled by a few people is a(n)

    a. dictatorship.

    b. democracy.

    c. monarchy.

    d. oligarchy.

_____ **4.** Someone who took power in an illegal way was a(n)

    a. aristocrat.

    b. oligarch.

    c. senator.

    d. tyrant.

_____ **5.** Solon helped prevent a revolt by making a law that no citizen could

    a. become king.

    b. earn more money than any other citizen.

    c. be enslaved for debt.

    d. leave Athens.

_____ **6.** The only Greeks who had the right to take part in ruling a city-state were

    a. citizens.

    b. helots.

    c. slaves.

    d. tyrants.

_____ **7.** A government in which a majority of the citizens make the decisions is a(n)

    a. aristocracy.

    b. democracy.

    c. monarchy.

    d. oligarchy.

_____ **8.** When someone was ostracized, they had to

    a. leave for ten years.

    b. leave forever.

    c. pay a fine.

    d. go to jail.

_____ **9.** The Council of 500 was made up of

    a. the 500 richest Athenians.

    b. the 500 oldest Athenians.

    c. the 500 wisest Athenians.

    d. 500 citizens chosen at random.

_____ **10.** Women, enslaved people, and people who had moved to Athens from other places could not

    a. wear shoes.

    b. take part in government.

    c. become doctors.

    d. purchase property.

SECTION 4
4

SECTION 4 QUIZ
Sparta and Athens

Multiple Choice
Choose the letter of the best answer.

_____ 1. A direct democracy was used to govern the Greek city-state of

    a. Athens.

    b. Marathon.

    c. Phoenicia.

    d. Sparta.

_____ 2. Athens' main rival was the city-state of

    a. Anatolia.

    b. Marathon.

    c. Sparta.

    d. Thermopylae.

_____ 3. The Spartans conquered a neighboring area and forced its residents to become

    a. colonists.

    b. slaves.

    c. soldiers.

    d. tyrants.

_____ 4. Spartan boys lived in military houses called

    a. acropolises.

    b. agoras.

    c. barracks.

    d. stoas.

_____ 5. Sparta focused on building a strong army because it feared a revolt by the

    a. barracks.

    b. helots.

    c. merchants.

    d. oligarchs.

_____ 6. The modern long-distance race named after a city in Greece that played an important role in the Persian Wars is called a(n)

    a. decathlon.

    b. marathon.

    c. olympics.

    d. triathlon.

_____ 7. In Athens, education was designed to prepare boys to become good

    a. citizens.

    b. sailors.

    c. soldiers.

    d. workers.

_____ 8. To defeat Persia, Athens worked together with

    a. Anatolia.

    b. France.

    c. Rome.

    d. Sparta.

_____ 9. Women in Sparta were expected to be

    a. beautiful.

    b. good cooks.

    c. quiet and obedient.

    d. emotionally and physically tough.

_____ 10. An army of 300 Spartans guarded a narrow pass at

    a. Athens.

    b. Crete.

    c. Marathon.

    d. Thermopylae.

SECTION 1

RETEACHING ACTIVITY

The Geography of Greece

A. Reading Comprehension

Find the name or term in the second column that best matches the description in the first column. Then write the letter of your answer in the blank.

_____ 1. a body of land that has water on three sides

_____ 2. the southern tip of Greece, which is connected to the rest of Greece by a narrow strip of land

_____ 3. the large sea that is south of Greece

_____ 4. the small sea that is east of Greece

_____ 5. one of the surplus goods that Greece traded for products such as timber, animal hides, and nuts

_____ 6. the most important city of the first Greek civilization

_____ 7. a narrow strip of land that connects two larger masses of land

_____ 8. a trading people who lived on the coast of the eastern Mediterranean and who influenced the early Greeks

_____ 9. the set of symbols that the Greeks developed into their own system of writing

_____ 10. metal objects invented in Anatolia about 650 B.C. for use in trade

a. Aegean
b. alphabet
c. coins
d. isthmus
e. Mycenae
f. Mediterranean
g. olive oil
h. Peloponnesus
i. peninsula
j. Phoenicians

SECTION
2
RETEACHING ACTIVITY
Life in Ancient Greece

A. Find Main Ideas
In the blank, fill in the name or term that correctly completes the sentence.

Athena	fire	Trojan War
epics	Mount Olympus	Zeus
fable	myth	

1. The Greeks believed _____ was the home of the major gods and goddesses.

2. The goddess _____ was the protector of Athens.

3. A story that people tell to explain beliefs about their world is called a _____.

4. The story of Prometheus provides an explanation for how humans came to have _____.

5. The Olympics were games that were held every four years to honor _____.

6. Long poems that tell stories of ancient heroes are called _____.

7. The *Iliad* portrays events during the _____.

8. A _____ is a short story, usually involving animals, that teaches a moral lesson.

SECTION

3 | The City-State and Democracy

RETEACHING ACTIVITY

A. Find Main Ideas

Complete the chart below by answering questions about the rise of city-states and the development of democracy in Greece.

Political Developments in Greece	
Rise of City-States	1. What is a city-state?
	2. What were the largest city-states in ancient Greece?
	3. What area was the center of city life?
	4. What was an acropolis?
Forms of Government	5. What was the earliest form of government in Greece?
	6. What is an oligarchy?
	7. In ancient Greece, what was a tyrant?
Athens Builds a Limited Democracy	8. How is the term *citizen* defined today?
	9. What kind of government allows citizens to make political decisions?
	10. In what way was Athens' democracy limited?

SECTION
4 | RETEACHING ACTIVITY
Sparta and Athens

A. Find Main Ideas

Find the name or term in the second column that best matches the description in the first column. Then write the letter of your answer in the blank.

_____ **1.** people who were defeated by Sparta and were forced to give Sparta half of their crops

_____ **2.** buildings that served as housing for boys being trained in the military

_____ **3.** type of government that developed in Athens over time

_____ **4.** the plain from which a runner ran to Athens to tell of the Greek victory over the Persians

a. barracks

b. direct democracy

c. helots

d. Marathon

B. Reading Comprehension

The following questions deal with the Greek city-states of Sparta and Athens. Answer them in the space provided.

5. How was Sparta's government structured?

_____

_____

_____

6. What did Spartan society expect of Spartan women?

_____

_____

_____

7. How were boys of wealthy Athenian families educated?

_____

_____

_____

CHAPTER
7

CHAPTER 7 TEST
Ancient Greece

Form A

Part 1: Multiple Choice
Choose the letter of the best answer. (4 points each)

_____ 1. Almost 80 percent of Greece is covered with

    a. farmland.

    b. forests.

    c. mountains.

    d. water.

_____ 2. One valuable natural resource that Greece had was

    a. diamonds.

    b. gold.

    c. silver.

    d. stone.

_____ 3. The goddess who protected Athens was

    a. Aphrodite.

    b. Athena.

    c. Demeter.

    d. Hera.

_____ 4. The *Iliad* is about the

    a. tortoise and the hare.

    b. journey that Odysseus made.

    c. attack on Troy by the Greeks.

    d. unjust suffering of Prometheus.

_____ 5. Many Greek fables were composed by

    a. Achilles.

    b. Aesop.

    c. Homer.

    d. Zeus.

_____ 6. The basic unit of government in Greece was the

    a. city-state.

    b. county.

    c. nation.

    d. township.

_____ 7. The center of city life in Greece was the

    a. agora.

    b. isthmus.

    c. Parthenon.

    d. peninsula.

_____ 8. A leader who made political reforms in Athens was

    a. Homer.

    b. Plutarch.

    c. Solon.

    d. Zeus.

_____ 9. Boys in Athens got an education to prepare them to become

    a. good citizens.

    b. kind fathers.

    c. military leaders.

    d. smart businessmen.

_____ 10. The lowest group in Spartan society was made up of

    a. boys.

    b. helots.

    c. soldiers.

    d. women.

CHAPTER 7 TEST A, *CONTINUED*

Part 2: Map Skills

Using the exhibit, choose the letter of the best answer. (4 points each)

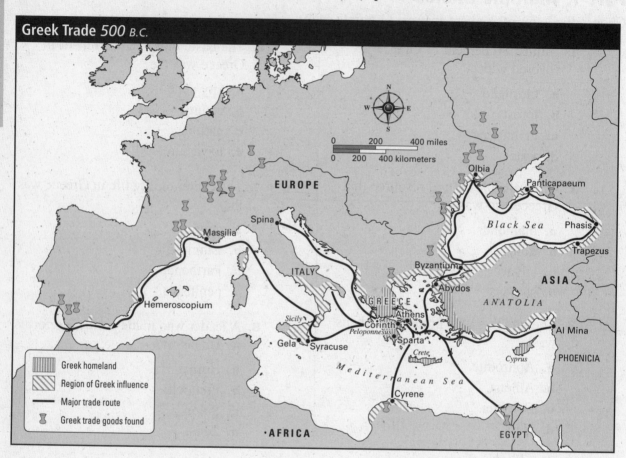

Greek Trade *500* B.C.

- Greek homeland
- Region of Greek influence
- Major trade route
- Greek trade goods found

_____ **11.** What does this map show?

    a. areas conquered by the Greeks

    b. battles of the Persian Wars

    c. climate zones of Greece

    d. patterns of Greek trade

_____ **12.** What North African city was in a region of Greek influence?

    a. Cyrene   **c.** Phoenicia

    b. Egypt   **d.** Sparta

_____ **13.** What city was located on Sicily?

    a. Al Mina   **c.** Gela

    b. Corinth   **d.** Olbia

_____ **14.** On what continents did the Greeks trade?

    a. Asia, Africa, and Europe

    b. Australia, Asia, and Africa

    c. North America, Asia, and Europe

    d. South America, Asia, and Africa

_____ **15.** What major waterways did the Greeks use for trade?

    a. Atlantic Ocean and Pacific Ocean

    b. Black Sea and Caspian Sea

    c. Mediterranean Sea and Black Sea

    d. North Sea and Black Sea

Part 3: Interpreting Charts

Using the exhibit, choose the letter of the best answer. (4 points each)

FORMS OF GOVERNMENT	
Monarchy	**Aristocracy**
• State is ruled by a king. • Rule is hereditary. • Some rulers claim divine right. • Form practiced in Mycenae (1450 B.C.).	• State is ruled by nobility. • Rule is hereditary and based on land ownership. • Social status and wealth support rulers' authority. • Form practiced in Athens (590 B.C.).
Oligarchy	**Limited Democracy**
• State is ruled by a small group of citizens. • Rule is based on wealth. • Ruling group controls the military. • Form practiced in Sparta (800–600 B.C.).	• State is ruled by its citizens. • Rule is based on citizenship. • Majority vote decides rule. • Form practiced in Athens (500 B.C.).

_____ **16.** In which form of government did social status play a role?

    a. aristocracy   **c.** monarchy

    b. direct democracy   **d.** oligarchy

_____ **17.** What form of government was practiced in Sparta?

    a. aristocracy   **c.** monarchy

    b. direct democracy   **d.** oligarchy

_____ **18.** Where was monarchy the form of government around 1450 B.C.?

    a. Athens   **c.** Rome

    b. Mycenae   **d.** Sparta

_____ **19.** Which form of government sometimes had a ruler who claimed divine right?

    a. aristocracy

    b. direct democracy

    c. monarchy

    d. oligarchy

_____ **20.** Which form of government was ruled by all citizens?

    a. aristocracy

    b. direct democracy

    c. monarchy

    d. oligarchy

Part 4: Document-Based Questions

INTRODUCTION

Historical Context Greek philosophers developed many ideas about democracy and other types of government. In Plato's *Republic*, characters try to decide on the best form of government. They discuss democracy but decide that it is not ideal. Plato's student, Aristotle, also wrote about the advantages and disadvantages of different types of governments.

TASK Understand Greek ideas about democracy.

A. Short Answer Study each document carefully and answer the questions that follow. (3 points each)

Document 1: Excerpt from Plato's *Republic*

And then democracy comes into being after the poor have conquered their opponents [the wealthy], slaughtering some and banishing some, while to the remainder they give an equal share of freedom and power; and this is the form of government in which the magistrates [officials] are commonly elected by lot....

And where freedom is, the individual is clearly able to order for himself his own life as he pleases?

Clearly.

Then in this kind of State there will be the greatest variety of human natures?

There will.

This, then, seems likely to be the fairest of States, being an embroidered robe which is spangled with every sort of flower. And just as women and children think a variety of colours to be of all things most charming, so there are many men to whom this State, which is spangled with the manners and characters of mankind, will appear to be the fairest of States.

---

21. According to Plato, what must the poor do before a society can become a democracy?

   _____

   _____

22. To what did Plato compare democracy?

   _____

   _____

Document 2: Excerpt from Aristotle's *Politics*

The basis of a democratic state is liberty; which, according to the common opinion of men, can only be enjoyed in such a state; this they affirm to be the great end of every democracy. One principle of liberty is for all to rule and be ruled in turn, and indeed democratic justice is the application of numerical not proportionate equality; whence it follows that the majority must be supreme, and that whatever the majority approve must be the end and the just. Every citizen, it is said, must have equality, and therefore in a democracy the poor have more power than the rich, because there are more of them, and the will of the majority is supreme. This, then, is one note of liberty which all democrats affirm to be the principle of their state.

23. According to Aristotle, what is the basis of a democracy?

_____

_____

Document 3: Relief showing Aristotle and Plato

24. What are Plato and Aristotle doing in this

image? _____

_____

_____

Source: *Plato and Aristotle or Philosophy* (1437–1439), Luca della Robbia the Elder. Relief from a series of the Liberal Arts at the Campanile of the Duomo. Museo dell'Opera del Duomo, Florence, Italy. Photo © Scala/ Art Resource, New York.

B. Essay Use information from the documents, your answers to the questions following the documents, and your knowledge of history to write an essay on the following topic. (8 points)

25. What are the benefits of democracy, according to Plato and Aristotle?

CHAPTER
7

CHAPTER 7 TEST

Ancient Greece

Form B

Part 1: Multiple Choice

Choose the letter of the best answer. (4 points each)

_____ 1. Greeks traded _____ for foreign items they needed.

  a. animal hides

  b. grain

  c. olive oil

  d. timber

_____ 2. _____ was the first Greek civilization.

  a. Athens

  b. Mycenae

  c. Phoenicia

  d. Sparta

_____ 3. _____ often were the main characters of Greek myths.

  a. Animals and people

  b. Gods and animals

  c. Gods and goddesses

  d. Animals and goddesses

_____ 4. The Olympics were named for _____.

  a. the leader of the gods

  b. the main temple in Athens

  c. the home of the gods

  d. a nearby sea

_____ 5. The original purpose of an acropolis was to _____.

  a. worship the gods

  b. house the king

  c. house common people

  d. protect the city

_____ 6. The government of Athens was an example of _____ democracy

  a. aristocratic

  b. direct

  c. indirect

  d. tyrannical

_____ 7. Only _____ could be citizens in Athens.

  a. adult helots

  b. adult women

  c. free adult men

  d. free elderly men

_____ 8. The distance between Marathon and Athens is about _____ miles.

  a. 5

  b. 15

  c. 25

  d. 50

_____ 9. The Persian Wars started when the Persians conquered _____.

  a. Anatolia

  b. Athens

  c. Sparta

  d. Thermopylae

_____ 10. The Greek ships in the battle at Thermopylae were _____ than those of the Persians.

  a. larger

  b. more mobile

  c. more numerous

  d. slower

CHAPTER 7 TEST B, *CONTINUED*

Part 2: Map Skills

Using the exhibit, answer the questions. (4 points each)

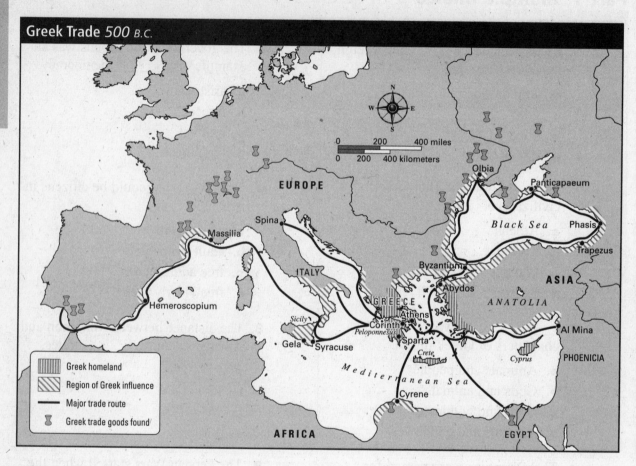

Greek Trade *500* B.C.

11. What city in northern Italy traded with the Greeks?

   a. Gela   c. Spina

   b. Massilia   d. Syracuse

12. What major island was part of the Greek homeland?

   a. Cyprus   c. Egypt

   b. Cyrene   d. Sicily

13. What body of water did the Greek trade route completely encircle?

   a. Black Sea

   b. Danube River

   c. Mediterranean Sea

   d. Nile River

14. What is the westernmost trade city labeled on the map?

_____

15. About how far apart were Athens and Syracuse?

_____

Part 3: Interpreting Charts

Using the exhibit, choose the letter of the best answer. (4 points each)

FORMS OF GOVERNMENT	
Monarchy	**Aristocracy**
• State is ruled by a king. • Rule is hereditary. • Some rulers claim divine right. • Form practiced in Mycenae (1450 B.C.).	• State is ruled by nobility. • Rule is hereditary and based on land ownership. • Social status and wealth support rulers' authority. • Form practiced in Athens (590 B.C.).
Oligarchy	**Limited Democracy**
• State is ruled by a small group of citizens. • Rule is based on wealth. • Ruling group controls the military. • Form practiced in Sparta (800–600 B.C.).	• State is ruled by its citizens. • Rule is based on citizenship. • Majority vote decides rule. • Form practiced in Athens (500 B.C.).

_____ 16. In which forms of government was rule based at least partially on wealth?

   a. oligarchy and monarchy
   b. democracy and aristocracy
   c. monarchy and aristocracy
   d. aristocracy and oligarchy

_____ 17. In which forms of government did heredity play no role in the selection of rulers?

   a. oligarchy and monarchy
   b. democracy and oligarchy
   c. monarchy and aristocracy
   d. aristocracy and democracy

_____ 18. Which form of government does not involve rule by a group?

   a. aristocracy   **c.** monarchy
   b. direct   **d.** oligarchy
       democracy

_____ 19. How did government in Athens evolve?

   a. aristocracy to democracy
   b. democracy to oligarchy
   c. monarchy to aristocracy
   d. oligarchy to aristocracy

_____ 20. Which form of government was the earliest in this region?

   a. aristocracy   **c.** monarchy
   b. direct   **d.** oligarchy
       democracy

CHAPTER 7 TEST B, *CONTINUED*

Part 4: Document-Based Questions

INTRODUCTION

Historical Context Greek philosophers developed many ideas about democracy and other types of government. In Plato's *Republic*, characters try to decide on the best form of government. They discuss democracy but decide that it is not ideal. Plato's student, Aristotle, also wrote about the advantages and disadvantages of different types of governments.

TASK Understand Greek ideas about democracy.

A. Short Answer Study each document carefully and answer the questions that follow. (3 points each)

Document 1: Excerpt from Plato's *Republic*

And then democracy comes into being after the poor have conquered their opponents [the wealthy], slaughtering some and banishing some, while to the remainder they give an equal share of freedom and power; and this is the form of government in which the magistrates [officials] are commonly elected by lot....

And where freedom is, the individual is clearly able to order for himself his own life as he pleases?

Clearly.

Then in this kind of State there will be the greatest variety of human natures?

There will.

This, then, seems likely to be the fairest of States, being an embroidered robe which is spangled with every sort of flower. And just as women and children think a variety of colours to be of all things most charming, so there are many men to whom this State, which is spangled with the manners and characters of mankind, will appear to be the fairest of States.

---

21. According to Plato, what has to happen before a society becomes a democracy?

_____

22. What makes democracy "the fairest of States"?

_____

Document 2: Excerpt from Aristotle's Politics

The basis of a democratic state is liberty; which, according to the common opinion of men, can only be enjoyed in such a state; this they affirm to be the great end of every democracy. One principle of liberty is for all to rule and be ruled in turn, and indeed democratic justice is the application of numerical not proportionate equality; whence it follows that the majority must be supreme, and that whatever the majority approve must be the end and the just. Every citizen, it is said, must have equality, and therefore in a democracy the poor have more power than the rich, because there are more of them, and the will of the majority is supreme. This, then, is one note of liberty which all democrats affirm to be the principle of their state.

23. According to Aristotle, who rules in a democracy?

_____

Document 3: Relief showing Aristotle and Plato

24. What does this image suggest about

Aristotle's and Plato's ideas? _____

_____

_____

Source: *Plato and Aristotle or Philosophy* (1437–1439), Luca della Robbia the Elder. Relief from a series of the Liberal Arts at the Campanile of the Duomo. Museo dell'Opera del Duomo, Florence, Italy. Photo © Scala/ Art Resource, New York.

B. Essay Use information from the documents, your answers to the questions following the documents, and your knowledge of history to write an essay on the following topic. (8 points)

25. How did Aristotle's ideas about democracy compare to those of Plato?

CHAPTER
7

CHAPTER 7 TEST

Ancient Greece

Form C

Part 1: Multiple Choice

Choose the letter of the best answer. (4 points each)

_____ 1. Which of the following seas borders Greece?

   a. Aegean

   b. Black

   c. Caspian

   d. Tyrrhenian

_____ 2. Why did landowners hold a high place in Greek society?

   a. They defended the homeland.

   b. They governed all the city-states.

   c. They controlled trade and wealth.

   d. They built the roads.

_____ 3. What led to the death of Achilles?

   a. a fall from a great height

   b. an epidemic in Greece

   c. a weak spot on his heel

   d. a boat accident

_____ 4. What was the purpose of fables?

   a. to teach people history

   b. to tell epic stories of the gods

   c. to encourage scientific thought

   d. to teach moral lessons

_____ 5. Which is true of city-states?

   a. They were mostly democracies.

   b. They started as oligarchies and became monarchies.

   c. They used different political systems.

   d. They were all the same.

_____ 6. How was education similar in Athens and Sparta?

   a. Boys and girls went to school.

   b. Boys started school at age seven.

   c. Girls trained to be mothers.

   d. Boys were trained to be soldiers.

_____ 7. Which of the following applies to the tyrants of ancient Greece?

   a. The common people supported them.

   b. The wealthy supported them.

   c. They always imposed harsh laws.

   d. They came to power legally.

_____ 8. What did Cleisthenes use to organize the citizens of Athens?

   a. place of residence

   b. order of birth

   c. wealth

   d. the status of their parents

_____ 9. What did the Spartan expression "Bring back this shield yourself or be brought back on it" mean?

   a. Capture an enemy's shield.

   b. Come back safely.

   c. Shield yourself from the enemy.

   d. Return victorious or die fighting.

_____ 10. What resulted from the Persian Wars?

   a. The Persians won.

   b. Athens was defeated.

   c. The Greeks united.

   d. Sparta was defeated.

CHAPTER 7

Part 2: Map Skills

Using the exhibit, answer the questions. (4 points each)

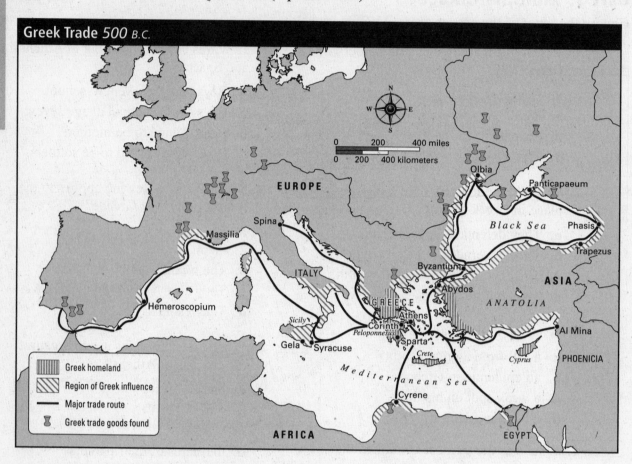

Greek Trade *500* B.C.

11. What does the map imply about the Greeks' abilities as sailors?

_____

12. What waterway did the Greeks use to trade goods with eastern Europe?

_____

13. Is it likely that more Greeks lived on Sicily or on Cyprus? Why?

_____

14. About how many miles was the sea route from Athens to Egypt?

_____

15. If a Greek ship left Sparta and followed a major trade route east, at what city
would it land?

_____

Part 3: Interpreting Charts

Using the exhibit, choose the letter of the best answer. (4 points each)

FORMS OF GOVERNMENT	
Monarchy	**Aristocracy**
• State is ruled by a king. • Rule is hereditary. • Some rulers claim divine right. • Form practiced in Mycenae (1450 B.C.).	• State is ruled by nobility. • Rule is hereditary and based on land ownership. • Social status and wealth support rulers' authority. • Form practiced in Athens (590 B.C.).
Oligarchy	**Limited Democracy**
• State is ruled by a small group of citizens. • Rule is based on wealth. • Ruling group controls the military. • Form practiced in Sparta (800–600 B.C.).	• State is ruled by its citizens. • Rule is based on citizenship. • Majority vote decides rule. • Form practiced in Athens (500 B.C.).

16. In which form of government was rule sometimes justified by religion?

_____

17. Why is the government during the time of Cleisthenes referred to as *limited democracy*?

_____

18. Why would Sparta's rulers have been difficult to overthrow?

_____

19. In which city-state was power most widely shared?

_____

20. What changes transformed Athens from an aristocracy into a limited democracy?

_____

CHAPTER 7

Part 4: Document-Based Questions

INTRODUCTION

Historical Context Greek philosophers developed many ideas about democracy and other types of government. In Plato's *Republic*, characters try to decide on the best form of government. They discuss democracy but decide that it is not ideal. Plato's student, Aristotle, also wrote about the advantages and disadvantages of different types of governments.

TASK Understand Greek contributions to democratic ideals.

A. Short Answer Study each document carefully and answer the questions that follow. (3 points each)

Document 1: Excerpt from Plato's *Republic*

And then democracy comes into being after the poor have conquered their opponents [the wealthy], slaughtering some and banishing some, while to the remainder they give an equal share of freedom and power; and this is the form of government in which the magistrates [officials] are commonly elected by lot....

And where freedom is, the individual is clearly able to order for himself his own life as he pleases?

Clearly.

Then in this kind of State there will be the greatest variety of human natures?

There will.

This, then, seems likely to be the fairest of States, being an embroidered robe which is spangled with every sort of flower. And just as women and children think a variety of colours to be of all things most charming, so there are many men to whom this State, which is spangled with the manners and characters of mankind, will appear to be the fairest of States.

---

21. According to Plato, how does democracy lead to diversity?

_____

_____

22. What must the poor do after conquering their opponents in order for democracy to come about?

_____

_____

Document 2: Excerpt from Aristotle's *Politics*

The basis of a democratic state is liberty; which, according to the common opinion of men, can only be enjoyed in such a state; this they affirm to be the great end of every democracy. One principle of liberty is for all to rule and be ruled in turn, and indeed democratic justice is the application of numerical not proportionate equality; whence it follows that the majority must be supreme, and that whatever the majority approve must be the end and the just. Every citizen, it is said, must have equality, and therefore in a democracy the poor have more power than the rich, because there are more of them, and the will of the majority is supreme. This, then, is one note of liberty which all democrats affirm to be the principle of their state.

23. What does Aristotle mean by "to rule and to be ruled in turn"?

_____

_____

Document 3: Relief showing Aristotle and Plato

24. What methods of teaching does this image

imply Plato used with Aristotle? _____

_____

_____

_____

Source: *Plato and Aristotle or Philosophy* (1437–1439), Luca della Robbia the Elder. Relief from a series of the Liberal Arts at the Campanile of the Duomo. Museo dell'Opera del Duomo, Florence, Italy. Photo © Scala/Art Resource, New York.

B. Essay Use information from the documents, your answers to the questions following the documents, and your knowledge of history to write an essay on the following topic. (8 points)

25. What do Plato and Aristotle say that might be interpreted as criticisms of democracy?

Starting with a Story

CHANGING TIMES

Background: Pericles (PEHR•ih•KLEEZ) has led Athens since about 460 B.C. One of his goals is to strengthen Athenian democracy. He proposed a plan to increase the number of paid political positions. When political positions are unpaid, only wealthy people can afford to serve. With the new plan, even poor citizens could serve in the government.

This suggested change has caused a lot of people to talk about how times are changing. Some people say it is good, but others don't agree. You have been asked by Pericles to go to the marketplace and listen to what citizens are saying about his plan.

Source: Illustration by Ezra Tucker

They were shouting. "Pericles wants more public officials to get paid," one of them hollered above the rest. "Poor citizens will start running the government of Athens. I don't like that!" The wealthy citizens were talking about the proposed policy change. Pericles was due to arrive at any moment. I was acting as his "eyes and ears " in the market place. Later, I would tell Pericles what I heard being said by the citizens of Athens.

"But I think Pericles is right," another man said. "Any citizen who wants to serve in the government should be able to do so. Pericles says being poor shouldn't prevent a man from serving our city."

"Yes," another man agreed. Several others nodded. "A poor man can serve Athens. Many poor men are just as intelligent as rich men. How can we ask the poor to obey our government if they cannot be public officials?"

"You're right. If a man is poor, it's not his fault!" piped up a fourth citizen. "Blame it on the gods!"

"Rich men are much better educated," a fifth man argued. "That's why only the rich should serve Athens."

Another man answered him. "But Pericles said that no one needs to be ashamed of poverty. The real shame is not trying to escape it."

Just then I heard footsteps. Pericles was coming! I needed to move away from the crowd. Later, he asked me if I had some advice for him based on what I heard. I knew what I would say and hoped he would agree with my advice.

What advice would you give Pericles?

Reading & Writing

1. **READING: Character and Plot** What character trait does Pericles show when supporting the rights of a poor citizen to serve in the government? What other character traits will he need to actually get the plan passed?

2. **WRITING: Persuasion** Think about what you heard. Think about the qualities needed to be a good public official. Then write a position paper outlining points that will help Pericles persuade people that his plan is the correct one.

SECTION
1

READING STUDY GUIDE

Athenian Democracy and War

- **Before, You Learned** Ancient Greece was not a unified country. It was made up of independent city-states. Two of the leading city-states were Athens and Sparta.

- **Now You Will Learn** Under the leadership of Pericles, Athens became the leading city-state of ancient Greece. Athens fought Sparta in the Peloponnesian War.

AS YOU READ Take notes on the main ideas of the section. Use the following graphic organizers.

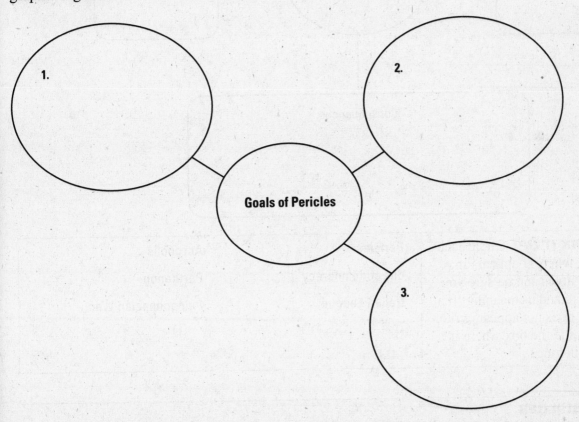

1.

2.

Goals of Pericles

3.

SECTION 1: ATHENIAN DEMOCRACY AND WAR, *CONTINUED*

CHAPTER 8

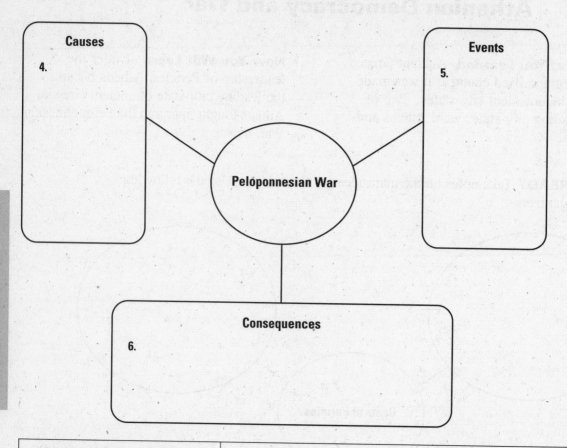

Causes

4.

Events

5.

Peloponnesian War

Consequences

6.

MARK IT UP! Circle each term where it appears in your notes and be sure you understand its meaning. If a term does not appear, write it beside the box where it best belongs.	Pericles	Acropolis
direct democracy	Parthenon
Delian League	Peloponnesian War

SKILLBUILDER

Source: © Kevin Schaefer/Corbis

7. **MARK IT UP!** Draw an arrow pointing to the Parthenon.

8. Write a caption that tells what part of Athens is pictured.

_____

_____

READING STUDY GUIDE
Alexander the Great

- **Before, You Learned** Athens and Sparta were the two leading city-states in Ancient Greece. They and their allies fought in the Peloponnesian War, which lasted from 431 to 404 B.C.

- **Now You Will Learn** Phillip II of Macedonia conquered Greece. His son, Alexander, built a huge empire across parts of Europe and Asia. Greek culture spread throughout Alexander's empire.

AS YOU READ Take notes listing the causes and effects in the section. Use the following graphic organizers.

Causes	Effects
New tactics and weapons	1.
Alexander destroyed Thebes	2.
Alexander conquered Anatolia, Egypt, Mesopotamia, and Persepolis	3.

Causes	Effects
4. Greeks ruled Alexander's empire. They blended . . .	Hellenistic culture
The knowledge of Greek, Egyptian, Arab, and Indian scientists was combined.	5.
6. The Temple of the Muses in Alexandria served as . . .	Scholars from throughout the Mediterranean area and Asia came to Alexandria to study.

SECTION 2: ALEXANDER THE GREAT, *CONTINUED*

MARK IT UP! Circle each term where it appears in your notes and be sure you understand its meaning. If a term does not appear, write it beside the box where it best belongs.	catapult Hellenistic Alexander the Great Alexandria

SKILLBUILDER

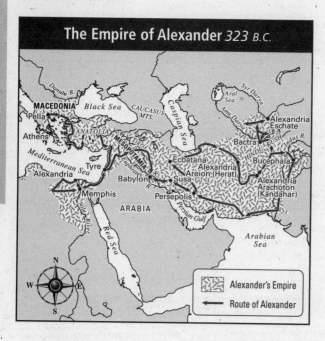

The Empire of Alexander 323 B.C.

7. **MARK IT UP!** Label Egypt, Persia, and India on the map.

8. What gulf lies near Persepolis?

   _____

9. Name the seas that bordered Alexander's empire.

   _____

   _____

CHAPTER 8

SECTION
3

READING STUDY GUIDE

The Golden Age of Greece

- **Before, You Learned** Trade helped the early Greeks develop a sophisticated culture. Early Greek literature included stories that taught lessons and long poems that told of adventures.

- **Now You Will Learn** Greek culture reached a peak in the 400s B.C. Greek achievements in architecture, literature, mathematics, and science from the foundation of Western Culture.

AS YOU READ Take notes listing the main ideas in the section. Use the following graphic organizers.

The Arts & Architecture	Democracy, History, & Philosophy	Science & Technology
1. Greek drama had two forms, . . .	3. Many Greek city-states adopted the style of government used in . . .	5. Ptolemy described a universe in which everything revolved around . . .
2. Greek artists tried to create a sense of . . .	4. In their search for the truth, the Greeks developed . . .	6. Euclid organized knowledge about . . .

CHAPTER 8

SECTION 3: THE GOLDEN AGE OF GREECE, *CONTINUED*

The Arts	History & Philosophy	Science & Technology
7. Dramatists	**9.** Historians	**11.** Astronomers
8. Artists	**10.** Philosophers	**12.** Mathematicians and Inventors

MARK IT UP! Circle each term where it appears in your notes and be sure you understand its meaning. If a term does not appear, write it beside the box where it best belongs.	drama tragedy comedy	ideal pediment philosophy

SKILLBUILDER

Source: © Bettmann/Corbis

13. *MARK IT UP!* This sculpture shows a girl with two pet birds. Circle the birds.

14. Write a caption for this image that describes how the sculpture shows characteristics of Greek art.

_____

_____

_____

READING STUDY GUIDE WITH ADDITIONAL SUPPORT
Athenian Democracy and War

Before, You Learned

Ancient Greece was not a unified country. It was made up of independent city-states. Two of the leading city-states were Athens and Sparta.

Now You Will Learn

Under the leadership of Pericles, Athens became the leading city-state of ancient Greece. Athens fought Sparta in the Peloponnesian War.

Preview Terms and Names

- **Pericles:** led Athens from 460 to 429 B.C.
- **direct democracy:** form of government in which all citizens participate
- **Delian League:** league of Greek city-states formed for mutual protection
- **Acropolis:** highest part of Athens, location of important temples, monuments, and buildings
- **Parthenon:** temple for Athena on the Acropolis
- **Peloponnesian War:** conflict between Athens and Sparta from 431 to 404 B.C.

Take Notes as You Read

Use this chart to take notes as you read.

a.

b.

1. Goals of Pericles

c.

Pericles Leads Athens

After the Persian Wars, Pericles became the strongest leader in Athens. Pericles wanted to strengthen democracy by spreading power more equally among Athenian citizens. He paid elected officials, so that even poor citizens could hold public office. He also wanted to expand Athens' power abroad and to beautify the city.

2. How did Pericles try to strengthen democracy?

_____

_____

SECTION 1: ATHENIAN DEMOCRACY AND WAR, *CONTINUED*

CHAPTER 8

Expanding the Empire

The Greek city-states formed the Delian League for mutual protection from Persia. Because Athens had the strongest navy, it took over leadership of the Delian League. The league's treasury was moved to Athens. As Athens gained more power, Pericles began turning the league into an Athenian empire.

3. How did Athens gain an empire?

_____

_____

Beautifying Athens

In order to rebuild and beautify Athens after the Persian Wars, Pericles took funds from the Delian League treasury. This action made the other members of the league angry. On the Acropolis, or "high city," Athenians built the Parthenon. The Parthenon was a temple to Athena and a masterpiece of architectural design.

4. How did Pericles pay for the rebuilding of Athens?

_____

_____

Peloponnesian War

Some city-states feared Athens' growing power. Sparta formed the Peloponnesian League to stand up to the Athenian empire. In 431 B.C., Sparta declared war on Athens. This conflict is called the Peloponnesian War.

Athens' strategy was to avoid land battles and rely on its sea power. Sparta, with a better land-based army, surrounded Athens and destroyed its crops. Early in the war, a plague, or disease, broke out in Athens. The plague killed about one-third of the people in Athens, including Pericles.

A truce was declared in 421 B.C., but fighting broke out again. Athens attacked Sicily in order to cut off supplies to Sparta. Later, Sparta destroyed Athens' navy. Athens finally surrendered to Sparta in 404 B.C.

5. What events weakened Athens during the Peloponnesian War?

_____

_____

Look Closer

Source: © Kevin Schaefer/Corbis

Mark It Up!

6. Draw an arrow pointing to the Parthenon.

7. Write a caption telling what part of Athens is pictured.

_____

_____

READING STUDY GUIDE WITH ADDITIONAL SUPPORT
Alexander the Great

Before, You Learned

Athens and Sparta were the two leading city-states in Ancient Greece. They fought each other in the Peloponnesian War from 431 to 404 B.C.

Now You Will Learn

Philip II of Macedonia conquered Greece. His son, Alexander, built an empire across Asia. Greek culture spread throughout the empire.

Preview Terms and Names

- **catapult:** military machine used to hurl stones or spears at enemy forces and city walls
- **Alexander the Great:** King of Macedonia who conquered parts of Europe, Africa, and Asia
- **Hellenistic:** culture made up of parts of Greek, Persian, Egyptian, and Indian styles and customs
- **Alexandria:** city in Egypt founded by Alexander in 332 B.C.

Take Notes as You Read

Use this chart to take notes as you read.

Causes	1. Effects
New weapons	a.
Destruction of Thebes	b.
Alexander's conquests	c.

The Kingdom of Macedonia

Philip II of Macedonia organized a well-trained professional army. He devised new tactics and used new weapons, such as the catapult. These advances gave his forces an advantage over other armies.

Philip conquered the Greek city-states, in part because the Greeks were weak and disorganized after the Peloponnesian War. Philip then prepared to attack Persia. However, in 336 B.C. Philip was assassinated, and his 20-year-old son, Alexander, took the throne.

2. Why were the Greek city-states vulnerable to Philip's attack?

_____

_____

SECTION 2: ALEXANDER THE GREAT, *CONTINUED*

Alexander Tries to Conquer the World

Alexander continued his father's plan of creating an empire. He defeated the Persians in Anatolia, then took Egypt from the Persians. He attacked Persepolis, the Persian capital. By 331 B.C., he controlled the Persian Empire.

Alexander continued to lead his armies eastward until he reached India. But his armies had been fighting for 11 years and refused to march further. Alexander and his troops returned to Babylon, where he died from a fever in 323 B.C. After Alexander's death, three key generals divided his empire.

3. Why did Alexander's empire end at India?

_____

_____

The Legacy of Alexander

Alexander's conquests helped to create a new culture. Alexander left Greeks behind to rule his lands. But Alexander and his armies adopted Persian clothing styles and customs. The blend of Greek, Persian, Egyptian, and Indian styles and customs became known as Hellenistic culture. The combined knowledge of the cultures led to new discoveries in science and medicine.

The most famous Hellenistic city was Alexandria, Egypt, which Alexander founded in 332 B.C. Alexandria served as an important center of learning for over 400 years.

4. How did Hellenistic culture develop?

_____

_____

_____

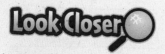

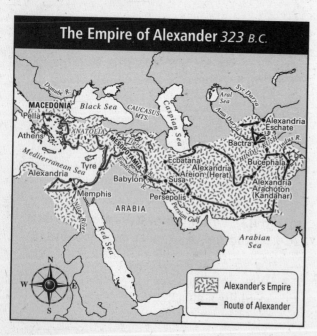

The Empire of Alexander *323 B.C.*

Alexander's Empire
→ Route of Alexander

5. Label Egypt, Persia, and India on the map.

3 | The Golden Age of Greece

READING STUDY GUIDE WITH ADDITIONAL SUPPORT

Before, You Learned

Trade helped the early Greeks develop a sophisticated culture. Early Greek literature included stories that taught lessons and long poems about heros.

Now You Will Learn

Greek culture reached a peak in the 400s B.C. Greek achievements in architecture, literature, mathematics, and science form the foundation of Western culture.

Preview Terms and Names

- **drama:** written work performed by actors
- **tragedy:** serious drama that presents the downfall of an important character
- **comedy:** humorous dramatic work that makes fun of politics, important people, or ideas
- **ideal:** perfected form
- **pediment:** triangular space between the top of a colonnade and the roof
- **philosophy:** logical study of basic truths about knowledge, values, and the world

Take Notes as You Read

Use this chart to take notes as you read.

1. The Arts & Architecture	Democracy, History, & Philosophy	Science & Technology
a. Greek drama had two forms, . . .	c. Many Greek city-states adopted the style of government used in . . .	e. Ptolemy described a universe in which everything revolved around . . .
b. Greek artists tried to create a sense of . . .	d. In their search for the truth, the Greeks developed . . .	f. Euclid organized knowledge about . . .

The Arts and Architecture

During the classical period—400s and early 300s B.C.—Greek writers, artists, and architects created great works. The Greeks invented drama as an art form and built the first theaters in the Western world. Greek drama had two forms: tragedy and comedy.

Greek artists tried to capture ideal forms. They tried to create a sense of order, beauty, and harmony in their work. Greek architects created buildings with graceful proportions, such as the Parthenon.

2. What are some characteristics of classical Greek art?

_____

_____

CHAPTER 8

Democracy, History, and Philosophy

After Athens developed democracy, other city-states began using that form of government. The Greeks' ideas on government have been adapted by many countries, including the United States.

The Greeks created some of the first and most important works of history and philosophy. Herodotus has been called the Father of History. Thucydides developed methods for writing history that are still used today. In their search for truth, the Greeks developed philosophy. Socrates encouraged people to examine their ideas by asking them question after question. Plato and Aristotle wrote great works and established important schools in Athens.

3. How did Athens influence modern ideas of government?

_____

_____

Science and Technology

By the 200s B.C., Alexandria, Egypt, had replaced Athens as the leading cultural center. Hellenistic scholars preserved and expanded scientific and mathematical knowledge.

The astronomer Ptolemy described the sun, planets, and stars as revolving around the earth. It took 1,400 years before scientists proved that the earth is not the center of the universe. The mathematician Euclid organized much of what was known about geometry into a set of books called *The Elements*. The first noted female mathematician, Hypatia, also taught at Alexandria.

4. What Egyptian city became a center of knowledge and education?

_____

_____

Look Closer

Source: © Bettmann/Corbis

5. Write a caption for this image, describing some qualities that are characteristic of Greek art.

_____

_____

_____

SECCIÓN
1

GUÍA DE ESTUDIO DE LECTURA

La democracia ateniense y la guerra

- **Antes aprendiste** La antigua Grecia no era una nación unificada. Estaba constituida por ciudades estado independientes. Dos de las ciudades estado más importantes eran Atenas y Esparta.

- **Ahora aprenderás** Bajo el liderazgo de Pericles, Atenas se convirtió en la ciudad estado principal de la antigua Grecia. Atenas luchó contra Esparta en la guerra del Peloponeso.

AL LEER Toma notas sobre las ideas principales de la sección. Usa las ayudas gráficas siguientes.

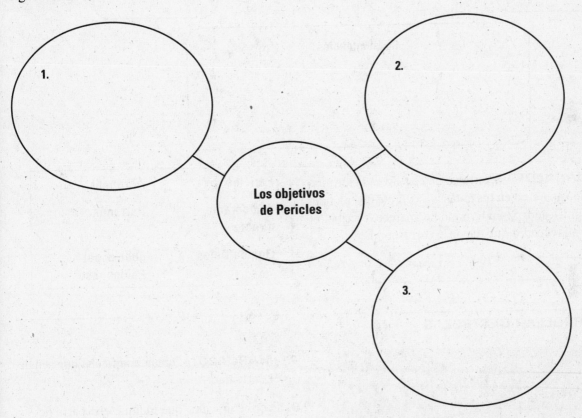

1.

2.

Los objetivos de Pericles

3.

CHAPTER 8

SECCIÓN 1: LA DEMOCRACIA ATENIENSE Y LA GUERRA, *CONTINUACIÓN*

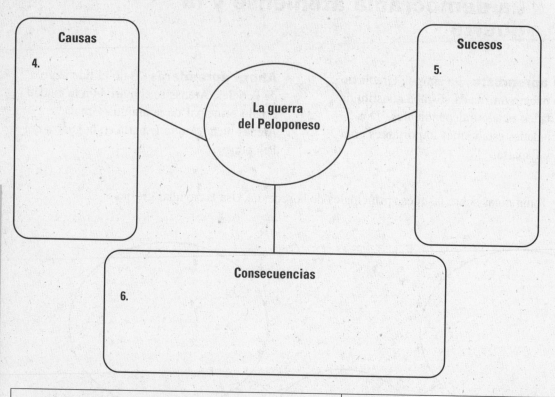

Causas

4.

La guerra del Peloponeso

Sucesos

5.

Consecuencias

6.

¡MÁRCALO! Encierra en un círculo cada término cuando aparezca en tus notas y asegúrate de entender su significado. Si un término no aparece, escríbelo junto al recuadro que mejor le corresponda.	Pericles	Acrópolis
	democracia directa	Partenón
	Liga de Delos	guerra del Peloponeso

DESARROLLAR DESTREZAS

Source: © Kevin Schaefer/Corbis

7. **¡MÁRCALO!** Dibuja una flecha que señale el Partenón.

8. Escribe un calce que indique qué parte de Atenas está representada.

_____

_____

CHAPTER 8

SECCIÓN
2

GUÍA DE ESTUDIO DE LECTURA
Alejandro Magno

- **Antes aprendiste** Atenas y Esparta eran las dos ciudades estado más importantes de la antigua Grecia. Se enfrentaron, junto con sus aliados, en la guerra del Peloponeso, que tuvo lugar entre los años 431 y 404 a.C.

- **Ahora aprenderás** Filipo II de Macedonia conquistó Grecia. Su hijo, Alejandro, construyó un imperio inmenso que abarcaba partes de Europa y de Asia. La cultura griega se difundió por el imperio de Alejandro.

AL LEER Toma notas donde enumeres las causas y los efectos presentados en esta sección. Usa las ayudas gráficas siguientes.

Causas	Efectos
Tácticas y armas nuevas	1.
Alejandro destruyó Tebas	2.
Alejandro conquistó Anatolia, Egipto, Mesopotamia y Persépolis	3.

SECCIÓN 2: ALEJANDRO MAGNO, *CONTINUACIÓN*

Causas	Efectos
4. Los griegos gobernaban el imperio de Alejandro. Fusionaron [...]	Cultura helenística
Se combinó el conocimiento de los científicos griegos, egipcios, árabes e hindúes.	5.
6. El templo de las Musas, en Alejandría, servía como [...]	Los eruditos del área del Mediterráneo y de Asia llegaban a Alejandría para estudiar.

¡MÁRCALO! Encierra en un círculo cada término cuando aparezca en tus notas y asegúrate de entender su significado. Si un término no aparece, escríbelo junto al recuadro que mejor le corresponda.	catapulta Alejandro Magno	helenístico Alejandría

DESARROLLAR DESTREZAS

El imperio de Alejandro, *323 a.C.*

MACEDONIA · Pela · Atenas · Mar Negro · MONTES CÁUCASO · Mar Caspio · Río Danubio · Mar Aral · Sir Daria · Amu Daria · Alejandría (Eschate) · Bactriana · Río Indo · Mar Mediterráneo · MESOPOTAMIA · Éufrates · Tigris · Tiro · Alejandría · Babilonia · Menfis · Ecbatana · Susa · Persépolis · ARABIA · Golfo Pérsico · Alejandría (Herat) · Bucéfala · Alejandría (Kandahar) · Mar Rojo · Mar Arábigo

N O E S

Imperio de Alejandro

Ruta de Alejandro

7. **¡MÁRCALO!** Pon un título a Egipto, Persia y la India en el mapa.

8. ¿Qué golfo se halla cerca de Persépolis?

_____

9. Nombra los mares que bordeaban el imperio de Alejandro.

_____

_____

SECCIÓN
3

GUÍA DE ESTUDIO DE LECTURA
La Edad de Oro de Grecia

- **Antes aprendiste** El comercio ayudó a los antiguos griegos a desarrollar una cultura sofisticada. La literatura griega antigua incluía relatos que transmitían enseñanzas, y extensos poemas de aventuras.

- **Ahora aprenderás** La cultura griega alcanzó su apogeo en el siglo V a.C. Los logros griegos en arquitectura, literatura, matemáticas y ciencias constituyen los cimientos de la cultura occidental.

AL LEER Toma notas donde enumeres las ideas principales de la sección. Usa las ayudas gráficas siguientes.

Las artes y la arquitectura	Historia, filosofía y democracia	Ciencias y tecnología
1. El drama griego tenía dos formas, [...]	3. Muchas ciudades estado griegas adoptaron el estilo de gobierno empleado en [...]	5. Ptolomeo describió un universo en el cual todo giraba alrededor de la [...]
2. Los artistas griegos intentaron crear un sentido de [...]	4. En su búsqueda de la verdad, los griegos desarrollaron [...]	6. Euclides organizó el conocimiento acerca de [...]

CHAPTER 8

SECCIÓN 3: LA EDAD DE ORO DE GRECIA, *CONTINUACIÓN*

Las artes	Historia y filosofía	Ciencias y tecnología
7. Dramaturgos	9. Historiadores	11. Astrónomos
8. Artistas	10. Filósofos	12. Matemáticos e inventores

¡MÁRCALO! Encierra en un círculo cada término cuando aparezca en tus notas y asegúrate de entender su significado. Si un término no aparece, escríbelo junto al recuadro que mejor le corresponda.	**drama** **tragedia** **comedia**	**ideal** **frontón** **filosofía**

DESARROLLAR DESTREZAS

Source: © Bettmann/Corbis

13. **¡MÁRCALO!** Esta escultura muestra a una niña con dos aves domesticadas. Encierra las aves en un círculo.

14. Escribe un calce para esta imagen donde describas de qué manera la escultura muestra las características del arte griego.

_____

_____

GUÍA DE ESTUDIO DE LECTURA CON APOYO ADICIONAL
La democracia ateniense y la guerra

Antes aprendiste

La antigua Grecia no era una nación unificada. Estaba compuesta por ciudades estado independientes. Dos de las ciudades estado principales eran Atenas y Esparta.

Ahora aprenderás

Bajo el liderazgo de Pericles, Atenas se convirtió en la ciudad estado más importante de la antigua Grecia. Atenas combatió contra Esparta en la guerra del Peloponeso.

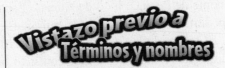
Vistazo previo a Términos y nombres

- **Pericles:** gobernó Atenas desde el año 460 hasta el año 429 a.C.
- **democracia directa:** forma de gobierno en la cual participan todos los ciudadanos
- **Liga de Delos:** liga de ciudades estado griegas formada para protegerse mutuamente
- **Acrópolis:** la parte más alta de Atenas, donde se hallan los edificios, templos y monumentos importantes
- **Partenón:** templo en honor a Atenea ubicado en la Acrópolis
- **Guerra del Peloponeso:** conflicto bélico entre Atenas y Esparta desde el año 431 hasta el año 404 a.C.

Tomar notas al leer

Usa este diagrama para tomar notas mientras lees.

a.

b.

1. Objetivos de Pericles

c.

Pericles gobierna Atenas

Después de las guerras contra Persia, Pericles se convirtió en el líder más poderoso de Atenas. Pericles quería fortalecer la democracia y distribuir el poder entre los ciudadanos atenienses. Les pagó un sueldo a los funcionarios públicos, para que incluso los ciudadanos pobres pudieran ejercer cargos públicos. También quería expandir el poder de Atenas en el extranjero y embellecer la ciudad.

2. ¿De qué manera Pericles intentó fortalecer la democracia?

_____

_____

SECCIÓN 1: LA DEMOCRACIA ATENIENSE Y LA GUERRA, *CONTINUACIÓN*

CHAPTER 8

Expandir el imperio

Las ciudades estado griegas formaron la Liga de Delos para protegerse mutuamente de Persia. Como Atenas tenía la flota más poderosa, asumió el liderazgo de la Liga de Delos. El tesoro de la liga se trasladó a Atenas. A medida que Atenas obtenía más poder, empezó a convertir a la liga en un imperio ateniense.

3. ¿Cómo obtuvo Atenas un imperio?

_____

Embellecer Atenas

Con el fin de reconstruir y embellecer Atenas después de las guerras contra Persia, Pericles tomó fondos del tesoro de la Liga de Delos. Esta acción hizo enfadar a las otras ciudades estado. Durante la reconstrucción de la Acrópolis, o "ciudad alta" de Atenas, los atenienses edificaron el Partenón. El Partenón, o templo en honor a Atenea, es una obra maestra del diseño arquitectónico.

4. ¿Cómo pagó Pericles la reconstrucción de Atenas?

_____

La guerra del Peloponeso

Algunas ciudades estado temían el poder creciente de Atenas. Esparta formó la Liga del Peloponeso para enfrentarse al imperio ateniense. En el año 431 a.C., Esparta le declaró la guerra a Atenas. Este conflicto bélico se denomina guerra del Peloponeso.

La estrategia de Atenas era evitar las batallas en tierra y confiar en su poder naval. Esparta, con un ejército terrestre superior, sitió Atenas y destruyó sus cultivos. En los primeros años de la guerra, un brote de peste, o enfermedad, se propagó en Atenas. La peste mató aproximadamente un tercio de los habitantes de Atenas, incluido Pericles.

Se declaró una tregua en el año 421 a.C., pero la lucha estalló nuevamente. Atenas atacó Sicilia para cortar el suministro de provisiones a Esparta. Posteriormente, Esparta destruyó la flota de Atenas. Atenas finalmente se rindió a Esparta en el año 404 a.C.

5. ¿Qué acontecimientos debilitaron a Atenas durante la guerra del Peloponeso?

_____

_____

De cerca 🔍

Source: © Kevin Schaefer/Corbis

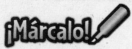

6. Escribe un calce que identifique el Partenón.

GUÍA DE ESTUDIO DE LECTURA CON APOYO ADICIONAL
Alejandro Magno

Antes aprendiste

Atenas y Esparta fueron las dos ciudades estado más importantes de la antigua Grecia. Combatieron una contra la otra en la Guerra del Peloponeso, desde el año 431 hasta el año 404 a.C.

Ahora aprenderás

Filipo II de Macedonia conquistó Grecia. Su hijo, Alejandro, construyó un imperio que se extendía por Asia. La cultura griega se difundió por todo el imperio.

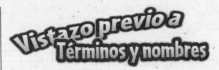
Vistazo previo a Términos y nombres

- **catapulta:** máquina militar empleada para arrojar piedras o saetas a las tropas enemigas y contra los muros de las ciudades
- **Alejandro Magno:** rey de Macedonia que conquistó partes de Europa, África y Asia
- **helenístico:** cultura constituida por elementos de los estilos y costumbres de Grecia, Persia, Egipto e India
- **Alejandría:** ciudad de Egipto fundada por Alejandro en el año 332 a.C.

Tomar notas al leer

Utiliza este diagrama para tomar notas mientras lees.

Causas	1. Efectos
Armas nuevas	a.
Destrucción de Tebas	b.
Conquistas de Alejandro	c.

El reino de Macedonia

Filipo II de Macedonia organizó un ejército profesional bien entrenado. Diseñó nuevas tácticas y empleó armas nuevas, como la catapulta. Estos progresos otorgaron a sus tropas una ventaja sobre sus enemigos.

Filipo conquistó las ciudades estado griegas, en parte porque los griegos estaban debilitados y desorganizados después de la Guerra del Peloponeso. Luego Filipo se preparó para atacar Persia. Sin embargo, en el año 336 a.C. Filipo fue asesinado y su hijo de 20 años de edad, Alejandro, llegó al trono.

2. ¿Por qué las ciudades estado griegas fueron vulnerables al ataque de Filipo?

_____

_____

SECCIÓN 2: ALEJANDRO MAGNO, *CONTINUACIÓN*

CHAPTER 8

Alejandro trata de conquistar el mundo

Alejandro continuó con el plan de su padre de crear un imperio. Derrotó a los persas en Anatolia y después se apoderó de Egipto, que estaba en manos de los persas. Atacó Persépolis, la capital de Persia. Hacia el año 331 a.C., controlaba el Imperio Persa.

Alejandro continuó dirigiendo sus tropas hacia el este, hasta que llegó a la India. Pero sus ejércitos habían estado combatiendo durante 11 años y se negaron a marchar más lejos. Alejandro y sus tropas regresaron a Babilonia, donde murió a causa de una fiebre en el año 323 a.C. Después de la muerte de Alejandro, sus tres generales principales dividieron su imperio.

3. ¿Por qué el imperio de Alejandro terminaba en la India?

_____

_____

El legado de Alejandro

Las conquistas de Alejandro contribuyeron a crear una nueva cultura. Alejandro designaba hombres griegos para que gobernaran sus tierras. Pero Alejandro y sus ejércitos adoptaron el estilo de vestimenta y las costumbres de los persas. La mezcla de estilos y costumbres provenientes de Grecia, Persia, Egipto y la India se denominó cultura helenística. El conocimiento combinado de las culturas condujo a nuevos descubrimientos en las ciencias y en medicina.

La ciudad helenística más famosa fue Alejandría, en Egipto, que Alejandro fundó en el año 332 a.C. Alejandría funcionó como un centro importante de aprendizaje durante más de 400 años.

4. ¿Cómo se desarrolló la cultura helenística?

_____

_____

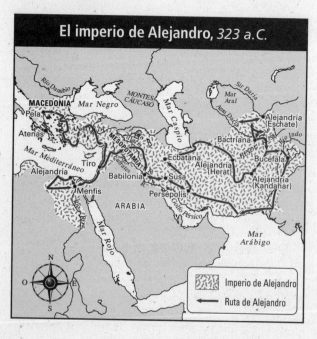

El imperio de Alejandro, *323 a.C.*

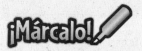

5. Rotula Egipto, Persia y la India en el mapa.

GUÍA DE ESTUDIO DE LECTURA CON APOYO ADICIONAL
La Edad de Oro de Grecia

Antes aprendiste

El comercio ayudó a los antiguos griegos a desarrollar una cultura sofisticada. La literatura griega antigua incluía relatos que transmitían enseñanzas y extensos poemas sobre héroes.

Ahora aprenderás

La cultura griega alcanzó su apogeo en el siglo V a.C. Los logros griegos en arquitectura, literatura, matemáticas y ciencias constituyen los cimientos de la cultura occidental.

Vistazo previo a Términos y nombres

- **drama:** obra escrita para ser representada por actores
- **tragedia:** obra de teatro seria que representa la caída de un personaje principal
- **comedia:** obra de teatro humorística que se burla de la política, las personas importantes o las ideas
- **ideal:** forma perfecta
- **frontón:** espacio triangular entre la parte superior de una columnata y el techo
- **filosofía:** estudio lógico de las verdades básicas acerca del conocimiento, los valores y el universo

Utiliza este diagrama para tomar notas mientras lees.

1. Las artes y la arquitectura	Historia, filosofía y democracia	Ciencias y tecnología
a. El drama griego tenía dos formas, [...]	c. Muchas ciudades estado griegas adoptaron el estilo de gobierno empleado en [...]	e. Ptolomeo describió un universo en el cual todo giraba alrededor de la [...]
b. Los artistas griegos intentaron crear un sentido de [...]	d. En su búsqueda de la verdad, los griegos desarrollaron [...]	f. Euclides organizó el conocimiento acerca de [...]

Las artes y la arquitectura

Durante el período clásico (siglo V e inicios del siglo IV a.C.), los escritores, artistas y arquitectos griegos crearon grandes obras. Los griegos inventaron el drama como una forma artística y construyeron los primeros teatros del mundo occidental. El drama griego tenía dos formas: tragedia y comedia.

Los artistas griegos intentaron capturar formas ideales. Trataron de crear en sus obras un sentido de orden, belleza y armonía. Los arquitectos griegos crearon edificios de elegantes proporciones, como el Partenón.

2. ¿Cuáles son algunas características del arte griego clásico?

_____

_____

SECCIÓN 3: LA EDAD DE ORO DE GRECIA, *CONTINUACIÓN*

Historia, filosofía y democracia

Después de que Atenas desarrolló la democracia, otras ciudades estado comenzaron a emplear esa forma de gobierno. Las ideas griegas sobre el gobierno han sido adoptadas por muchos países, incluidos los Estados Unidos.

Los griegos crearon algunas de las primeras y más importantes obras de historia y filosofía. Herodoto ha sido llamado el Padre de la Historia. Tucídides desarrolló métodos para escribir historia que se siguen utilizando en la actualidad. En su búsqueda de la verdad, los griegos desarrollaron la filosofía. Sócrates animaba a las personas a examinar sus ideas haciéndoles una pregunta tras otra. Platón y Aristóteles escribieron grandes obras y fundaron escuelas importantes en Atenas.

3. ¿De qué manera Atenas influenció las ideas actuales sobre el gobierno?

_____

_____

_____

Ciencias y tecnología

Hacia el siglo III a.C., Alejandría, en Egipto, había reemplazado a Atenas como principal centro cultural. Los eruditos helenísticos preservaron y ampliaron el conocimiento científico y matemático.

El astrónomo Ptolomeo describió que el Sol, los planetas y las estrellas giraban alrededor de la Tierra. Pasaron 1,400 años antes de que los científicos pudieran probar que la Tierra no es el centro del universo. El matemático Euclides organizó gran parte del conocimiento existente acerca de la geometría en una colección de libros denominada *Los elementos*. La primera mujer importante en el campo de las matemáticas, Hypatia, también enseñó en Alejandría.

4. ¿Qué ciudad egipcia se convirtió en un centro de conocimiento y educación?

_____

_____

De cerca

Source: © Bettmann/Corbis

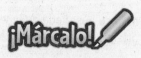

5. **Escribe** un calce para esta imagen donde describas algunas características típicas del arte griego.

_____

_____

_____

BUILDING BACKGROUND VOCABULARY
Classical Greece

compound	league	strategy
glorify	proportions	troupe
hostage	sponsor	tutored

A. Fill In the Blanks Choose the word that most accurately completes each sentence. Write that word in the blank provided.

1. After the Persian War, the Greek city-states formed a _____ for mutual protection.

2. Pericles ordered a program of construction to rebuild, beautify, and _____ Athens.

3. In the Peloponnesian War, Athens' _____ was to avoid battles on land and to rely on its sea power.

4. As a teenager, Philip II of Macedonia had been held _____ by the Greek city-state of Thebes.

5. The Greek philosopher Aristotle _____ Alexander the Great.

6. In Classical Greece, wealthy citizens would _____ the production of plays.

7. Each play was assigned to a different _____ of actors.

8. Greek architects created beautiful buildings with graceful _____.

9. Archimedes developed the _____ pulley, which harnessed the strength of multiple pulleys.

CHAPTER
8 | VOCABULARY PRACTICE
Classical Greece

A. Vocabulary

Complete the word search puzzle using words from Chapter 8 in the list below.

Across

1. Acropolis
2. Parthenon
3. Hellenistic
4. ideal
5. drama
6. comedy
7. tragedy

```
I  W  D  O  H  E  P  K  C  T  Z
L  R  K  D  M  Z  A  Q  I  W  L
U  I  D  E  A  L  R  A  T  C  T
A  C  M  E  I  N  T  C  S  V  H
M  C  C  V  T  O  H  R  I  L  Y
A  I  O  C  R  V  E  O  N  R  E
R  Q  M  O  A  H  N  P  E  Q  N
D  N  T  M  G  Q  O  O  L  I  X
L  Y  V  E  E  Y  N  L  L  U  R
D  C  D  D  D  P  N  I  E  F  B
I  B  P  Y  Y  G  P  S  H  W  V
```

B. Study Guide

Write the terms, names, or phrases that best complete the sentences.

8. I was the leader of Athens during its Golden Age. Who am I?

_____

9. I built one of the largest empires in the ancient world. Who am I?

_____

10. We are the three most famous philosophers from ancient Greece. Who are we?

_____

11. _____ is the form of government developed and used in

Athens.

12. Athens and Sparta and their allies fought each other in the

_____ War.

13. A great center of learning was established at _____ in Egypt.

CHAPTER 8

CHAPTER
8 | SKILLBUILDER PRACTICE
Classical Greece

Assessing Credibility of Sources

We get our information from many different sources, such as the Internet, newspapers, books, and friends. You can't always be sure that the information you get is accurate. So you must be an informed reader. You can determine how likely it is that the material you're reading is accurate by evaluating the sources.

There are some basic questions you can ask to help you decide if the information is likely accurate and balanced in its viewpoint. These questions work for both printed material and for sources on the Internet. One basic question you should ask is who is the author of the material. Sources such as encyclopedias, universities, and the government are usually reliable sources of information. Some groups and individuals try to convince you to accept their views without providing accurate information. If you find a source by an individual or group you have not heard of, try to find out if they are reliable and balanced in their views. Do some research to see if others think the author is an expert in the field.

Look below at the list of Internet resources on Alexander the Great found on a search engine and answer the questions. (See Skillbuilder handbook, page R29.)

Source 1: Alexander the Great—A History by 3 high school students
Source 2: *Encyclopaedia Britannica* 11th Edition—article on Alexander the Great
Source 3: *The Encyclopedia of Greece and the Hellenistic Tradition* by Kenneth Meyer
Source 4: Macedonia and Greece by "jojo"
Source 5: Who was Alexander the Great?—Official Republic of Macedonia site

QUESTIONS

1. Which source is run by a government?

_____

2. Which sources listed would probably be good and reliable sources of information?

_____

3. Which sources would you eliminate based on authorship? Explain

_____

_____

4. What additional information might you want to know about the author of Source 3?

_____

_____

CHAPTER 8

HISTORY MAKERS
Aristotle

The Philosopher

Aristotle (384–322 B.C.) was a great Greek philosopher. One of the world's most brilliant thinkers, he expanded many fields of knowledge.

Source: The Granger Collection, New York

Aristotle was born in northern Greece. His father was the royal physician and a friend of the Macedonian king. Aristotle was introduced to court life at an early age. When he was 17, Aristotle went to Athens, where he enrolled in a famous school known as the Academy.

Education Athens was a great center of learning, and the Academy was especially well known. The philosopher Plato had started the Academy and taught there as well. Among the subjects students learned were arithmetic, geometry, and astronomy. The Academy was similar to our modern colleges and universities.

Plato's search for the nature of truth and goodness was of special interest to Aristotle, and he remained at the Academy for 20 years. Although Plato considered Aristotle to be his best student, Aristotle was not selected to replace Plato when he died. Aristotle was not chosen to lead the school because he had developed too many of his own ideas. Some of these ideas moved away from the teachings of Plato. So, Aristotle left the Academy and taught at a school on the coast of Anatolia.

A Famous Pupil In 342 B.C., Aristotle received a royal invitation. Philip II, the king of Macedonia, asked Aristotle to become the teacher of his 13-year-old son, Alexander (who later became known as Alexander the Great). Aristotle accepted and once again found himself at a royal court. He taught Alexander a number of subjects, including politics, ethics, and science.

Alexander also studied the classics of Greek literature. He became especially fond of the *Iliad*, an epic poem about the siege of Troy. As an adult he visited Troy to honor the *Iliad's* heroes. After Alexander became king, he gave Aristotle a large sum of money to open his own school.

The Lyceum Aristotle used the money he received from Alexander to open the Lyceum, a school in Athens. Aristotle equipped the Lyceum with both a museum and a library. In the library were the written constitutions of 158 states, many of which were Greek. Aristotle himself wrote the Constitution of Athens, which was rediscovered in 1890. This document has helped scholars learn about the history of Athens.

Quotes from Aristotle When he taught, Aristotle had a habit of walking as he spoke. His students often walked with him as they discussed various subjects. People took to calling the Lyceum the peripatetic school. *Peripatetic* means to walk around.

Aristotle and his students discussed topics like happiness, justice, and the meaning of life. Here is a sample of some of his ideas.

- A friend is a second self.
- All men by nature desire understanding. A sign of this is their liking of sensations.
- Happiness depends upon ourselves.
- The only stable state is the one in which all men are equal before the law.

A Brilliant Mind Aristotle had a brilliant mind. His followers at that time called him "the Philosopher" or "the master of them that know." He classified knowledge into branches such as psychology (which for him was the study of the soul) and physics. Aristotle believed that knowledge comes from the senses

CHAPTER 8

and that observation is an important tool for learning. He believed this to be especially true for the "new" sciences, such as botany, zoology, and geography.

We know from Aristotle's writings that he used firsthand observation and dissection to learn about animals. He used these observations to develop a system of classifying animals. Much of his work in zoology—the study of animals—is consistent with modern science. One example is his description of the social interaction within a colony of bees. Aristotle's study and classification of animals formed the basis of zoology up until the 1800s.

Aristotle's Writings Aristotle is believed to have written 150 to 200 books, some of which were probably lecture notes. They covered subjects ranging from rhetoric—the art of speaking and writing—to politics, ethics, logic, and science. Students of philosophy still study many of Aristotle's works.

Not all of Aristotle's ideas turned out to be right. For example, he thought that underground winds caused earthquakes. Yet he was capable of both detailed observation and grand theories. His idea that the universe had no beginning and will not end suggests a modern theory that the universe is constantly expanding.

After the decline of Roman civilization, knowledge of the Greek language was almost completely lost. Few were able to read Aristotle's works. Then, in the 800s, Arabic translations of Greek works introduced Aristotle to the Islamic world. Those translations and some ancient Greek manuscripts eventually ended up it Italy. Scholars used Aristotle's writings to teach grammar, logic, and rhetoric. In the 1200s, Thomas Aquinas (uh•KWY•nuhs) introduced some of Aristotle's ideas into the teachings of the Roman Catholic church.

Exile Aristotle was highly respected in his own time. Yet at the end of his life he fell

victim to an outbreak of anti-Macedonian feeling. Aristotle thought that the killing of one famous Greek philosopher, Socrates, was one too many. (Socrates was forced to drink poison in 399 B.C.) Fearing for his life, Aristotle fled to Euboea (yoo•BEE•uh), an island in the Aegean Sea. A year later, he died.

CRITICAL THINKING QUESTIONS

1. **Find Main Ideas** Who was Aristotle's teacher?

2. **Summarize** What school did Aristotle establish and where was it located?

3. **Categorize** What method did Aristotle use to learn about the natural world?

4. **Evaluate** Which of Aristotle's achievements do you find most impressive? Explain your choice.

5. **Form and Support Opinions** Choose a quote from Aristotle and explain its meaning.

6. **Draw Conclusions** In what ways have Aristotle's ideas "stood the test of time"?

CONNECT GEOGRAPHY & HISTORY
Classical Greece

The Acropolis

The word *acropolis* originally referred to a fortified hill within a city. It often included a palace and temples to the gods. During the Persian War, the Persians destroyed many of the buildings on the Athenian Acropolis. After the war, Pericles convinced the citizens of Athens to build or rebuild temples at the site

To enter the Athenian Acropolis a visitor would pass through the Propyla, a central entryway with a double row of columns. Once inside, the first thing visitors saw was an enormous bronze statue of Athena. Known as Athena Promachos (Athena the Leading Warrior), the statue stood about thirty feet high. It could be seen from the sea by travelers arriving in Athens.

Temples to many gods, including Athena, Zeus, and Artemis, rested on the Acropolis. The Parthenon was the first temple Pericles ordered to be built. It was dedicated to Athena, the protector goddess of Athens. The Parthenon sits near the site of an earlier temple dedicated to Athena. Another large statue of Athena was placed inside the temple. Crafted from ivory and gold, the statue was about thirty feet high.

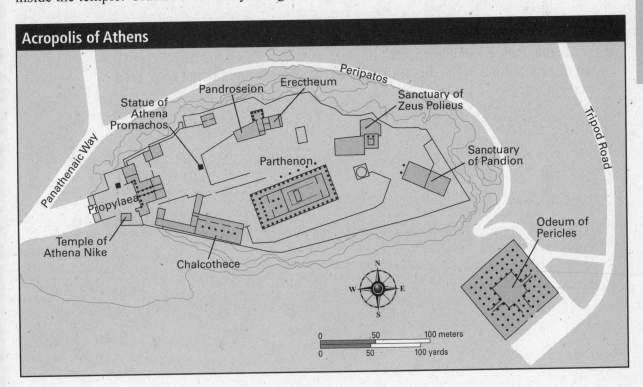

Acropolis of Athens

CONNECT GEOGRAPHY & HISTORY, *CONTINUED*

PRACTICE

Use the map to do these activities and answer these questions.

1. Which road runs closest to the Propyla?

_____

2. Which statue would visitors see directly ahead after passing through the Propyla?

_____

3. What are the approximate dimensions of the Parthenon?

_____

4. Which building is further north, the Sanctuary of Pandion or the Erectheum?

_____

5. Circle the location of the temple of Athena Nike.

APPLY

6. Study the photograph on page 212 in your textbook. Using the map, identify the three buildings at the top of the picture. If you need additional help, refer to the illustration on pages 172-173.

CHAPTER 8

CHAPTER
8

OUTLINE MAP ACTIVITY
Classical Greece

The Peloponnesian Wars, 431–404 B.C.

A. Label the Map Use the map on textbook page 214 to locate the following physical features, political regions, city-states, and historical battles. Then label them on the outline map that follows. Also, title your map and fill in the legend with the appropriate information.

Physical Features	Political Regions	City-States	Historical Battles
Aegean Sea	Greece	Athens	Amphipolis (422 B.C.)
Black Sea	Macedonia	Byzantium	Cynossema (411 B.C.)
Ionian Sea	Persian Empire	Corinth	Cyzicus (410 B.C.)
Mediterranean Sea		Ephesus	Notium (407 B.C.)
		Miletus	Spartalos (429 B.C.)
		Sparta	Sphacteria (425 B.C.)
		Thebes	

B. Questions After labeling your map, use it to answer the following questions.

1. What two city-states were the main combatants in the Peloponnesian War?

_____

2. Which of the two city-states had the most allies around the Aegean Sea?

_____

3. Which of the battles shown on this map took place first?

_____

4. How many battles shown on this map did each side win?

_____

5. What about the battle at Sphacteria might have worried the Spartans?

_____

_____

6. About how far is it between Athens and the most distant Athenian victory?

_____

7. Which battle was further north: Amphipolis or Cyzicus?

_____

8. How long did the Peloponnesian War last?

_____

9. Would the war have lasted that long if the two sides had modern weapons and transportation? Explain.

_____

10. What place shown on this map rose to power after the Peloponnesian War was finished?

_____

CHAPTER 8

OUTLINE MAP ACTIVITY, *CONTINUED*

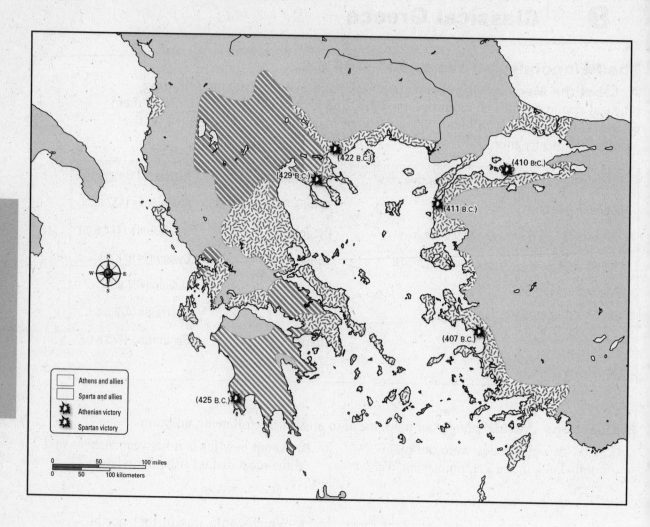

Legend:
- Athens and allies
- Sparta and allies
- ✳ Athenian victory
- ✳ Spartan victory

Map labels: (422 B.C.), (429 B.C.), (410 B.C.), (411 B.C.), (407 B.C.), (425 B.C.)

Scale: 0 50 100 miles / 0 50 100 kilometers

CHAPTER
8

OUTLINE MAP ACTIVITY
Classical Greece

Mediterranean Region

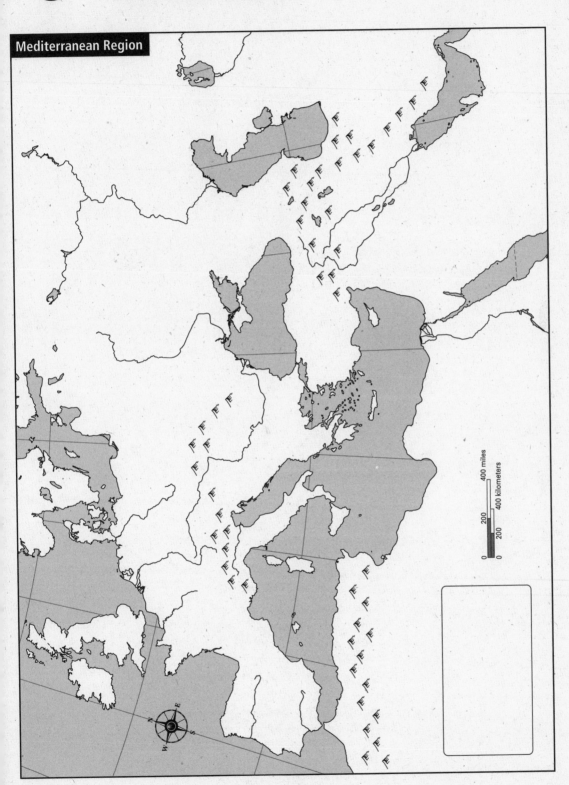

400 miles
200
400 kilometers
0   200
0

CHAPTER
8

PRIMARY AND SECONDARY SOURCES
Classical Greece

Pericles' Funeral Oration

At the end of the first year of the Peloponnesian War, the Athenians held an elaborate funeral for all those killed in the war. The funeral oration over these dead was delivered by the brilliant politician and general, Pericles. The Funeral Oration contains the patriotic feelings held by most Athenians.

For in the hour of trial Athens alone among her contemporaries is superior to the report of her. No enemy who comes against her is indignant [angry] at the reverses which he sustains at the hands of such a city; no subject complains that his masters are unworthy of him. And we shall assuredly not be without witnesses; there are mighty monuments of our power which will make us the wonder of this and succeeding ages; we shall not need the praises of Homer or of any other *panegyrist* [person who gives a tribute at a funeral] whose poetry may please for the moment, although his representation of the facts will not bear the light of day. For we have compelled every land and every sea to open a path for our valor, and have everywhere planted eternal memorials of our friendship and or our enmity [hatred]. Such is the city for whose sake these men nobly fought and died; they could not bear the thought that she might be taken from them; and every one of us who survives should gladly toil on her behalf.

excerpt from "Pericles' Funeral Oration" from *The Peloponnesian War* by Thucydides, translated by Benjamin Jowett

DOCUMENT–BASED QUESTIONS

1. **Analyze Point of View** Why does Pericles think that a defeated enemy will not feel bad about being beaten by the Athenians?

   _____

   _____

2. **Summarize** What reasons does Pericles give to support his claim that Athens will be "the wonder of this and succeeding ages"?

   _____

   _____

3. **Find Main Ideas** In which line does Pericles say that Athens is even better than people say it is?

   _____

   _____

4. **Compare and Contrast** Is this oration like one a U.S. president might give today during wartime? Why or why not?

   _____

   _____

CHAPTER
8 | LITERATURE
Classical Greece

CHAPTER 8

Oedipus the King by Sophocles

Sophocles' *Oedipus the King* is probably the most famous tragedy ever written. In the play Oedipus, king of Thebes, begins investigating the death of the earlier ruler of Thebes, Laius. Oedipus discovers that he was the one who had killed Laius. He also learns that Laius was his father. In the passage below, Oedipus describes how he unknowingly killed his own father.

> I will tell you all that happened there, my lady.
> There were three highways
> Coming together at a place I passed;
> And there a herald came towards me, and a chariot
> Drawn by horses, with a man such as you describe
> Seated in it. The groom leading the horses
> Forced me off the road at his lord's command;
> But as this charioteer lurched over towards me
> I struck him in my rage. The old man saw me
> And brought his double goad [an animal prod] down upon my head
> As I came abreast. He was paid back and more!
> Swinging my club in this right hand I knocked him
> Out of his car, and he rolled on the ground.
> I killed him. . . . I killed them all.
> Now if that stranger and Laius were—kin [relatives],
> Where is a man more miserable than I?
> More hated by the gods? Citizen and alien alike
> Must never shelter me or speak to me—
> I must be shunned by all.

from Oedipus Rex, *Sophocles, trans. Dudley Fitts and Robert Fitzgerald*

CRITICAL THINKING

1. **Summarize** What caused Oedipus to attack the man in the chariot and his groom?

_____

2. **Find Main Ideas** What punishment does Oedipus say he should suffer?

_____

3. **Make Inferences** How does Oedipus feel about what he did?

_____

4. **Form an Opinion** Why is *Oedipus the King* considered a tragedy?

_____

INTERDISCIPLINARY PROJECT
The Pythagorean Theorem

During classical times, Greek thinkers sought to understand the world. One of these thinkers was Pythagoras (pih•THAG•uhr•uhs) (c. 569 B.C.—c. 475 B.C.). As a result of his studies, he proved or developed several important mathematical rules. The Pythagorean Theorem was one of them. Although the Babylonians knew about this idea 1,000 years earlier, historians believe that Pythagoras and his followers were the first to prove it.

The Pythagorean Theorem states that the square of the hypotenuse, or long side, of a right triangle is equal to the sum of the squares of the other two sides. The theorem is expressed like this: $a^2 + b^2 = c^2$. The "2" next to the letters means "squared." You square a number by multiplying it by itself. That gives you the area covered by a square with sides of that length. For example, a square with 3-inch sides would have an area of 9 square inches.

The inverse of the square is the square root, which tells you for a square of a given area, how long each side is. Another way of looking at it is that the square root shows for a given number what other number multiplied by itself will equal the given number. For example, a

square with an area of 16 square inches would have 4-inch sides.

If you know the length of a and b, you can use the Pythagorean Theorem to find the length of c. For the triangle shown here, $a^2 = 81$, $b^2 = 144$, and $81 + 144 = 225$. The square root of 225 is 15, so $c = 15$.

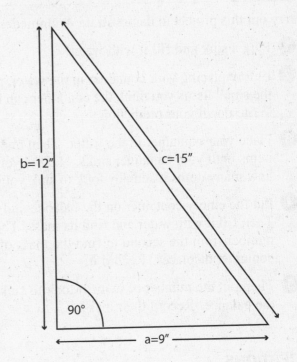

Project

Apply the Pythagorean Theorem to solve the problems below. Use a calculator to find the square roots, as needed.

1 **Problem A:** a = 3, b = 4; solve to find c

Problem B: a = 6, b = 8; solve to find c

Problem C: a = 5, b = 12; solve to find c

2 A baseball diamond is 90 feet on each side. How many feet does the catcher have to throw the ball from home plate to get a runner out at second base?

3 Create your own word problem that can be solved using the Pythagorean Theorem. Exchange your problem with a partner and solve. Review your work together to check your problems and answers.

INTERDISCIPLINARY PROJECT
Archimedes' Principle

CHAPTER 8

Archimedes (287–212 B.C.) was a Greek inventor and mathematician. One of his most famous discoveries is called Archimedes' Principle. It states that a body in a fluid is held up by a force equal to the mass of the fluid it displaces. This principle, or scientific rule, explains why objects—even very large ones, such as cruise ships or whales—float.

Project

Carry out this project to demonstrate Archimedes' Principle.

1. Plug a sink and fill it with water.

2. Before placing your container in the water, predict how many of the small items you think the container can hold before it sinks. Write down your prediction.

3. Place your container in the water. Then one by one, add small items until your container sinks. Next to your prediction, record how many items it actually took to sink your container.

4. Put the empty container on the balance and record its mass. Then fill it with water and find its mass. Then subtract the first number from the second to find the mass of the water your container displaces. Record it.

5. Then put the number of items it took to sink the container on the balance. Record their mass.

MATERIALS
• sink with plug
• small plastic or paper containers, such as margarine tubs or paper cups
• coins, pebbles, metal nuts, or other small items
• water
• balance and scale
• pencil and paper

QUESTIONS

1. What do you notice about the mass of the displaced water and mass of the items it took to sink the container? How does this demonstrate Archimedes' Principle?

2. Repeat the activity. This time predict how many items it will take to nearly sink your container. Explain your results.

3. Repeat the activity using different-sized containers—one larger and one smaller. Test your predictions about the number of items needed to sink them.

4. How do you think Archimedes' Principle is important in ship design?

INTERDISCIPLINARY PROJECT
War Headlines

8C Connect to Language Arts

Headlines are a way to capture your attention and draw you into reading more about a topic or event. Often, you will choose to read some material because the headline made you want to know more. The Greeks did not have newspapers or the Internet. They learned about an event by hearing the news from people who witnessed it.

In this exercise, we will imagine that the Greeks did have newspapers and that news of the Peloponnesian War was of great interest to them. Use the samples below to help you imagine other headlines for war events.

Daily Chronicle

Countryside Torn Apart by Spartan Armies

Athens, Greece—

...nicle

Rumors of a Spartan-Persian Alliance

Daily Chronicle   Page 13

Food Shortages Continue in Athens

Project

Report the details of several of the events of the Pelponnesian War. Follow these steps to create your headlines.

1. To become familiar with headline styles, examine pages of a newspaper or magazine or look at a news site on the Internet.

2. Make a list of four to six events that occurred during the Peloponnesian War.

3. Make notes about details of the event that may help you create the headlines.

4. Think about the audience that will read your headlines. What can you say in the headlines that will interest them?

5. Remember that the first word of a headline is important. Choose it carefully.

6. Share your headlines with a partner, and decide if the headlines make you want to know more about the events.

CHAPTER
8 | INTERDISCIPLINARY PROJECT
Advocating a Form of Government

Each city-state in ancient Greece was independent. The style of government varied from city-state to city-state, but there were three major forms of government.

- **Monarchy:** A king or queen had absolute power. This ruler could ask for advice, but his or her decisions could not be challenged.

- **Oligarchy:** A few people ruled. To be part of this group, a person had to be an aristocrat, own land, or possess great wealth.

- **Direct democracy:** All citizens met to decide on the laws. However, only free adult males were considered citizens and could participate in government.

Form of Government	Who Ruled	Basis for Rule	Type of Rule
Monarchy	king or queen	mandate from god; inheritance	Monarch had supreme power.
Oligarchy	a small group of citizens	aristocratic birth, wealth, or land ownership	Ruling group ran government for their own benefit.
Direct Democracy	all citizens (but not all people were citizens)	citizenship	Decisions made by voting; majority ruled.

Project

Take the role of a citizen of an ancient Greek city-state. Decide which form of government you think would be best for the people of your city-state. Decide how you would organize your government, and speak in favor of your choice to your fellow citizens. Follow these steps.

1 Review the types of government above.

2 Based on what you know about ancient Greece and the challenges of life at that time, decide which type of government you would support.

3 Make a chart showing how your government would be organized.

4 Write a short statement that urges people to agree with your choice. Your statement should give your reasons for supporting this form of government.

CHAPTER 8

8A Connect to Math
The Pythagorean Theorem

8B Connect to Science
Archimedes' Principle

OBJECTIVES

- To understand the Pythagorean Theorem
- To solve problems using the Pythagorean Theorem

OBJECTIVES

- To understand Archimedes' Principle
- To make and test hypotheses and observe results

STRATEGIES FOR THE MATH TEACHER

1. Distribute Project 8A to the class and give students a few minutes to read the materials. Review with the students the features of a right-angle triangle. If necessary, discuss how the letters a, b, and c stand for length of each side.

2. Using the values given for the model triangle, work through the steps to demonstrate how to find the length of c. Review, if necessary, square roots.

3. After students have created, solved, and checked one another's problems, have volunteers share their problems with the class.

STRATEGIES FOR THE SCIENCE TEACHER

1. Distribute Project 8B to the class. Give students a few minutes to read the materials.

2. Discuss with students why items float in water.

3. Divide the class into pairs and distribute the materials.

4. Demonstrate the process to students before they begin working.

ANSWERS

1. A. c = 5
   B. c = 10
   C. c = 13

2. about 127 feet; the actual distance on a major-league field is 127 ft 3 3/8"

ANSWERS

1. The mass of the items should be slightly greater. It shows that the container is held up by a force equal to the mass it displaces, but when that mass is exceeded, the container sinks.

2. To keep the container a float, the mass of the items needs to equal the mass of the displaced water.

3. Answers will vary, but should show that smaller containers need a lesser mass and larger containers need a greater mass of items to sink.

4. Ships have to be designed to hold only as much as they displace in the water.

RUBRIC

Students should be able to

- demonstrate an understanding of the Pythagorean Theorem
- solve problems by applying the Pythagorean Theorem

RUBRIC

Students should be able to

- understand Archimedes' Principle
- predict and explain how changing variables might produce different results

CHAPTER 8

8C Connect to Language Arts
War Headlines

OBJECTIVES

- To identify the event and create an appropriate headline
- To use newspaper style in creating headlines
- To write a headline that creates interest

STRATEGIES FOR THE LANGUAGE ARTS TEACHER

1. Collect examples of newspaper and magazine headlines. Have them ready for students to examine.
2. Distribute Project 8C to the class and have students read the material.
3. Have resources available to help with the research. Give students time to research events in the Peloponnesian War.
4. Remind students to keep the headlines short.
5. When students have completed final drafts, allow time for them to share their work.

RUBRIC

Students should be able to

- write a headline that highlights an event in the Peloponnesian War
- write a headline that creates interest in learning more about the event
- write in a newsworthy style

8D Connect to Civics
Advocating a Form of Government

OBJECTIVES

- To summarize three types of government found in ancient Greek city-states
- To analyze types of government and choose one to advocate
- To prepare materials to aid in defending and promoting a chosen type of government

STRATEGIES FOR THE CIVICS TEACHER

1. Distribute Project 8D and give students a few minutes to read the materials.
2. Review the types of government discussed in the activity.
3. Ask for suggestions about what the organization chart for the forms of government might include. (Distribution of power, hierarchy of authority)
4. Remind students that their statements should be brief. A statement of government preferred with bulleted items to support the statement is a practical format.
5. Display students' work.

RUBRIC

Students should be able to

- analyze the forms of city-states government and choose one to advocate
- create an organization chart for the form of government chosen that includes clear indication of distribution of power and hierarchy of authority
- include logical points to support the given choice of government

BRINGING SOCIAL STUDIES ALIVE
Cultural Collages

The Hellenistic and classical Greek cultures still shape the modern world. The headings that appear in the textbook lend themselves to independent exploration: Alexander's legacy of Hellenistic culture; classical Greek art and architecture; classical Greek history and philosophy; Greek and Hellenistic science and technology. Students can create collages presenting main ideas and conclusions about the four topics.

MATERIALS
• art supplies: crayons, markers, paint, glue
• poster board
• construction paper and plain paper
• scissors
• reference materials on Greek and Hellenistic culture

Week 1: Choose a Cultural Subject to Research (30–45 minutes) Hold a class discussion about the Hellenistic and Greek cultural legacies. Point out that important ideas and styles of thinking developed that guide artists, philosophers, and scientists today. Use these questions to encourage a focus on ideas and cultural styles

- How did Hellenistic culture blend different cultures?
- How do Greek art forms influence styles in Western culture today?
- What did Greek thinkers contribute in the fields of history and philosophy?
- How was science affected by Hellenistic knowledge?

Tell students that they can help others understand these important cultural influence by making collages. The collages will cover main ideas about Hellenistic culture and each of the three subheadings about the legacy of Greece.

Have students form groups of four. Ask each group to choose one of the following topics: Hellenistic culture; Greek drama; the visual arts and architecture; history; philosophy; or science and technology. Encourage groups to look for additional information in reference books and encyclopedias. Have students sketch or list their findings.

Week 2: Decide What to Present (30–45 minutes) Tell groups that the collages may combine written descriptions (75 words or less) of styles, brief biographies (75 words or less), sketches or images of discoveries or inventions, and pictures. A main heading should appear on each collage. Groups should complete their research and gather the supplies they will need for their collages.

Week 3: Make Collages (45–60 minutes) Have students sketch or print any pictures they wish to present and compose their written statements. Groups should then make their collages. As these near completion, tell the groups that they will need to accompany their collages with an informative discussion for the entire class.

Week 4: Display and Discuss (45–60 minutes) Display the collages in the classroom for viewing. Allow time for reading and study of each collage. Then ask the makers of each collage to hold brief discussions in turn. Encourage comments or questions from other class members.

BRINGING SOCIAL STUDIES ALIVE
Alexander's Empire Today

Geography Activity

In this chapter, you learned about the conquests of Alexander the Great. In this activity, you will use a map to identify the modern-day countries that exist in the locations of Alexander's conquests.

MATERIALS
• outline map of Greece, Northern Africa, and Central Asia showing outlines of modern countries
• colored pencils or markers
• atlases

1. Reread the paragraphs in the textbook about Alexander's conquests. Look at the map on page 219 of your textbook to identify or estimate the location of the conquered areas.
2. Using a pencil or marker of a color you have not yet used, draw a line on your map to indicate Alexander's empire. You can make a good guess about the location by locating rivers, seas, and latitude and longitude lines on the maps.
3. Lightly shade in the entire empire.
4. Use an atlas to find the modern-day countries that now occupy the areas once controlled by Alexander.
5. Print the modern-day names of countries on the map in the correct locations.
6. Make a legend for your map showing Alexander's empire and the modern-day countries.
7. Give your map a title.

BRINGING SOCIAL STUDIES ALIVE

Hands-On Activity

Build a Model Parthenon and Acropolis

Introduction

Is there a special site or beautiful building near your home? Chapter 8 tells you that Pericles took great pride in rebuilding the Acropolis. The Parthenon especially represented the wealth and power of Athens. Study the picture of the Acropolis on page 212 of Chapter 8. The Parthenon is the many columned building at the highest point of the hill. You can build a model of the Parthenon and a part of the Acropolis.

MATERIALS
• cardboard, cardboard tubes
• modeling clay
• construction paper
• small cartons, small boxes
• scissors
• glue
• paint, crayons

GETTING STARTED

1. Reread the paragraphs about the Acropolis in your textbook. If you have time, look for additional pictures of the Acropolis in reference books.
2. Make a list of the details about the Parthenon. For example, how many columns does it have? How does it appear in relation to other buildings of the Acropolis? What kind of roof does it have?
3. Make a sketch of the Parthenon.
4. Using your sketch to help you, make a model of the Parthenon.
5. Shape the clay to make a hill with a flat top. Place the model on it.

CHECKLIST

❑ My model Acropolis and Parthenon are similar to the picture shown on page 212.

❑ My model shows how the Parthenon stands upon a high hill.

❑ My model shows how the Parthenon stands in relation to other structures of the Acropolis.

CHAPTER **8** | BRINGING SOCIAL STUDIES ALIVE
Make Models of Greek Columns

Hands-On Activity

Introduction

Have you seen buildings with columns that look like the ones Greek architects designed? Page 231 of Chapter 8 shows you a building that copies the Greek style. Study the pictures of Greek columns on page 225 of your textbook. You can make models of Greek columns.

MATERIALS
• cardboard, cardboard tubes
• construction paper
• white paint, crayon, marker
• scissors
• glue

1. Reread the description of Greek architecture in your textbook. Be sure you understand the differences among the columns in the illustration on the same page. If you have time, look for additional pictures of Greek designs for columns in reference books.

2. Look carefully at the details on each column. Make a list of the details for the column you choose for your model. How is each column designed at the top?

3. Make a sketch of how your column should look.

4. Make models of the column using art materials. For example, you can use thin strips of construction paper to make the lines for your column. You can roll paper at the ends to make a scroll.

5. Make a written label to identify the kind of column you copied.

CHECKLIST

❑ My model is similar to the design of one kind of Greek column.
❑ My model tells something about the proportions of Greek columns.

BRINGING SOCIAL STUDIES ALIVE

Alexander's Welcome-Back Banquet

Introduction

Imagine you have traveled back to an exciting time in world history. You are in Babylon in 323 B.C. Alexander of Macedon has just returned from his farthest Persian conquests. He has not yet fallen ill with the strange illness from which he dies days later.

For your banquet, begin with the script that follows. Develop additional dialogue by rereading the text about Philip II of Macedon and his son, Alexander the Great. Reread especially the text that tells you how Alexander built an empire. Be sure your dialogue reflects what you have learned. If you have time, you may wish to refer to reference sources.

MATERIALS
• resource books on the life of Alexander the Great

Cast of Characters

Alexander

2 Generals

3 Friends

3 Guests

The Scene: You attend a banquet held to celebrate Alexander's return after building an immense empire. Others present at the banquet are family, friends, distinguished guests, and some generals of Alexander's troops.

Friend #1: Alexander, people said you were too young to take over leadership when your father died. After all, you were only 20 years old. What did you think back then?

Alexander: I knew I could lead. I was qualified for the job. I had the best tutors.

General #1: Did you have a favorite tutor?

Alexander: I really liked Lysimachus (ly•SIHM•uh•kuhs). He made up a game that let me pretend to be the hero Achilles. My mother Olympias (oh•LIHMP•pee•us) told me that the great Greek warrior Achilles was my ancestor. She was a princess from western Greece. Later, when I was about 13, my father sent me the last tutor I had, Aristotle. He was a Greek philosopher and scientist. Aristotle tutored me for three years.

Guest #1: Yes, but were you trained in military and government service? You had to be able to govern your father's conquered peoples and the Macedonian troops.

Alexander: When I was 16, I served as regent for my father. I didn't see him much when I was growing up. He was always on some military campaign. When I was 18, I led the cavalry at the Battle of Chaeronea (KEHR•uh•NEE•uh). We beat the city-states of Athens and Thebes combined. So I knew a lot about winning a war.

Friend #2: It must have been a terrible shock, the way your father died.

Alexander: Yes, a bodyguard murdered him at my sister's wedding. I was there.

Guest #2: Didn't your father build a great Macedonian army?

Alexander: He did. My father had figured out new ways of fighting. He had the soldiers attack in rectangular formations of eight men deep, called phalanxes (FAY•LANGKS•uhs). The soldiers carried heavy spears much longer than the enemies' spears. Besides, the soldiers used catapults and battering rams. The cavalry took part, too.

General #2: Alexander used many of the same methods for our battles against the Persians.

[*End, first part of dialogue.*]
Now, you fill in the dialogue about Alexander's conquests. Finish with the following dialogue:

Guest #3: Alexander, where will you lead your troops next?

Alexander: I plan to conquer Carthage and maybe Rome.

Friend #3: Well, even if you don't, you've already built a huge empire. You can be proud of that. Alexander, you're great.

[*The End*]
Have members of the class perform the banquet scene. If you can, celebrate Alexander's success with a real banquet. Alexander liked Greek ways and spread Greek culture wherever he went, so you might serve Greek food. Here are some suggestions: gyros, grapes, olives, goat cheese, fish, Greek salad, rolls and honey.

SECTION
1

SECTION 1 QUIZ
Athenian Democracy and War

Multiple Choice

Choose the letter of the best answer.

_____ 1. One of Athens' greatest leaders, _____ , emerged after the Persian Wars.

    a. Alexander

    b. Philip II

    c. Pericles

    d. Sophocles

_____ 2. In Athenian direct democracy, _____ participated in running the government.

    a. all citizens

    b. elected representatives

    c. only the wealthy

    d. only the nobles

_____ 3. The Greek city-states formed the _____ for mutual protection.

    a. Acropolis

    b. Delian League

    c. Parthenon

    d. Persian Compact

_____ 4. The important monuments and temples of Athens were built on the _____ , or the "high part."

    a. Acropolis

    b. Agora

    c. Delian League

    d. Parthenon

_____ 5. The Greeks built the _____ to honor the goddess Athena.

    a. Acropolis

    b. Agora

    c. Delian League

    d. Parthenon

_____ 6. Pericles asserted that what mattered in public service was the _____ which a man possesses.

    a. actual ability

    b. influence

    c. land

    d. money

_____ 7. Sparta and its allies fought the Athenian empire in the _____ War.

    a. Athenian-Spartan

    b. Mediterranean

    c. Persian

    d. Peloponnesian

_____ 8. Athens had a better _____ and avoided land battles.

    a. army

    b. fortress

    c. navy

    d. supply of arrows

_____ 9. A _____ started in 430 B.C. and killed about one-third of the people in Athens.

    a. battle

    b. fire

    c. flood

    d. plague

_____ 10. The Peloponnesian War lasted for _____ years.

    a. 5

    b. 13

    c. 27

    d. 48

CHAPTER 8

SECTION
2

SECTION 2 QUIZ
Alexander the Great

Multiple Choice

Choose the letter of the best answer.

_____ 1. A military machine that hurled stones or spears at enemy forces was the

    a. battering ram.

    b. catapult.

    c. legion.

    d. phalanx.

_____ 2. The Macedonian ruler who conquered the Greek city-states and ended their democratic practices was

    a. Alexander.

    b. Pericles.

    c. Philip II.

    d. Sophocles.

_____ 3. In order to build his empire, Alexander had to defeat

    a. Egypt.

    b. Greece.

    c. India.

    d. Persia.

_____ 4. Alexander's empire stretched from

    a. Egypt to Persia.

    b. Macedonia to Arabia.

    c. Greece to India.

    d. Mesopotamia to Persia.

_____ 5. The culture that blended Greek, Persian, Egyptian, and Indian influences was

    a. Arabian.

    b. European.

    c. Grecian.

    d. Hellenistic.

_____ 6. The most famous of the Hellenistic cities was the Egyptian city of

    a. Alexandria.

    b. Athens.

    c. Sparta.

    d. Thebes.

_____ 7. Philip II organized a well-trained professional

    a. acting troupe.

    b. army.

    c. gladiator corps.

    d. navy.

_____ 8. After it rebelled, Alexander destroyed the Greek city-state of

    a. Athens.

    b. Crete.

    c. Sparta.

    d. Thebes.

_____ 9. Alexander the Great died at age

    a. 20.

    b. 32.

    c. 56.

    d. 78.

_____ 10. The Temple of the Muses in Alexandria became famous for its

    a. columns.

    b. library.

    c. statues.

    d. zoo.

SECTION

3
SECTION 3 QUIZ
The Golden Age of Greece

Multiple Choice
Choose the letter of the best answer.

____ 1. _____ is a written work designed for actors to perform.

    a. Architecture

    b. Drama

    c. Geometry

    d. Philosophy

____ 2. In a _____, an important character experiences a downfall.

    a. comedy

    b. geometry

    c. philosophy

    d. tragedy

____ 3. Greek _____ often made fun of politics, important people, or ideas.

    a. comedies

    b. philosophy

    c. sculpture

    d. tragedies

____ 4. The Greeks developed _____, the logical study of basic truths and ideas about the world.

    a. comedy

    b. drama

    c. philosophy

    d. tragedy

____ 5. Greek artists worked to capture the perfect form, or the _____ , in their artwork.

    a. column

    b. ideal

    c. masterwork

    d. philosophy

____ 6. Aristophanes wrote _____ that made fun of people in power.

    a. comedies

    b. histories

    c. phiilosophy

    d. tragedies

____ 7. _____ claimed that his only wisdom lay in realizing how little he actually knew.

    a. Aristophanes

    b. Herodotus

    c. Ptolemy

    d. Socrates

____ 8. Ptolemy supported the idea that the _____ was at the center of the universe.

    a. earth

    b. Milky Way

    c. moon

    d. sun

____ 9. Euclid organized much of what was known about _____ into a set of books called the *Elements*.

    a. drama

    b. geometry

    c. history

    d. philosophy

____ 10. _____ explained the law of the lever and invented a water-lifting device.

    a. Archimedes

    b. Euclid

    c. Phidias

    d. Plato

SECTION 1 | RETEACHING ACTIVITY
Athenian Democracy and War

A. Find Main Ideas

In the blank, fill in the name or term that correctly completes the sentence.

Acropolis	direct democracy	plague
Athens	navy	Sparta
Delian League	Peloponnesian War	truce
	Pericles	

1. _____ wanted to strengthen Athens' democracy and expand its empire.

2. Athens had a _____, meaning that citizens actively participated in running the government.

3. After the Persian Wars, Greek city-states formed the _____ for mutual protection.

4. In Athens, the _____ was the location of important temples and monuments.

5. When Sparta declared war on Athens in 431 B.C., it marked the beginning of the _____.

6. Athens' war strategy relied on its superior _____.

7. In 430 B.C., a _____ broke out in Athens, killing about one-third of its population.

8. In 421 B.C., Athens and Sparta signed a _____, or an agreement to stop fighting, but battles soon raged again.

9. _____ finally surrendered to _____ in 404 B.C.

SECTION

2 | Alexander the Great

RETEACHING ACTIVITY

A. Find Main Ideas

The following questions deal with the rise of a new power to the north of Greece in Macedonia. Answer them in the space provided.

1. What made Philip of Macedonia a strong and successful military leader?

_____

_____

2. What steps did Alexander take to conquer the Persian Empire?

_____

_____

3. How did Alexander's actions help bring about the development of Hellenistic culture?

_____

_____

B. Reading Comprehension

Find the name or term that best matches the description. Then write the letter of your answer in the blank.

_____ 4. city founded in Egypt in 332 B.C., which had a library containing collections of Greek, Persian, Egyptian, and Hebrew texts

_____ 5. military machine that hurled stones or spears at the enemy

_____ 6. culture that blended Greek, Persian, Egyptian, and Indian styles and customs

_____ 7. Greek goddesses who ruled the arts and sciences

_____ 8. building in Alexandria that was considered one of the Seven Wonders of the World

a. Alexandria
b. catapult
c. Hellenistic
d. lighthouse
e. Muses

SECTION
3 | RETEACHING ACTIVITY
The Golden Age of Greece

A. Find Main Ideas

Complete the chart below by providing details about the legacy of Greece.

Greek Contributions	Details
Drama	1.
Architecture	2.
History	3.
Astronomy	4.
Mathematics	5.

B. Reading Comprehension

Find the name or term that best matches the description. Then write the letter of your answer in the blank.

_____ **6.** what Greek artists tried to capture by portraying perfect forms

_____ **7.** in architecture, the triangular space between the top of a colonnade and the roof

_____ **8.** the logical study of basic truths about knowledge, values, and the world

_____ **9.** Greek philosopher who asked people question after question

_____ **10.** inventor of the compound pulley and other useful devices

a. Archimedes
b. the ideal
c. pediment
d. philosophy
e. Socrates

CHAPTER 8 TEST
Classical Greece

CHAPTER 8

Part 1: Multiple Choice

Choose the letter of the best answer. (4 points each)

_____ 1. Pericles' goals for Athens included
   a. strengthening the monarchy.
   b. beautifying Athens.
   c. building wealth by raising taxes.
   d. increasing the power of the wealthy.

_____ 2. The original purpose of the Delian League was to
   a. conquer new lands for Athens.
   b. protect the city-states.
   c. improve agricultural production.
   d. build new temples and buildings.

_____ 3. The Parthenon housed a statue of
   a. Aphrodite.
   b. Athena.
   c. Hera.
   d. Zeus.

_____ 4. The Peloponnesian War was mainly fought between
   a. Athens and Macedonia.
   b. Egypt and Macedonia.
   c. Sparta and Athens.
   d. Persia and Athens.

_____ 5. The plague in Athens killed many people, including
   a. Alexander.
   b. Pericles.
   c. Philip II.
   d. Socrates.

_____ 6. The Macedonian leader who first conquered Greece was
   a. Alexander the Great.
   b. Pericles.
   c. Philip II.
   d. Sophocles.

_____ 7. The city founded by Alexander that became a center of Hellenistic culture was
   a. Alexandria.
   b. Athens.
   c. Memphis.
   d. Thebes.

_____ 8. An artform invented by the Greeks was
   a. architecture.
   b. drama.
   c. poetry.
   d. sculpture.

_____ 9. A question-and-answer style of teaching is sometimes called
   a. logic.
   b. the Plato's Academy.
   c. philosophy.
   d. the Socratic Method.

_____ 10. The historian who chronicled the Peloponnesian War was
   a. Alexander.
   b. Hippocrates.
   c. Thucydides.
   d. Socrates.

Part 2: Map Skills

Using the exhibit, choose the letter of the best answer. (4 points each)

CHAPTER 8

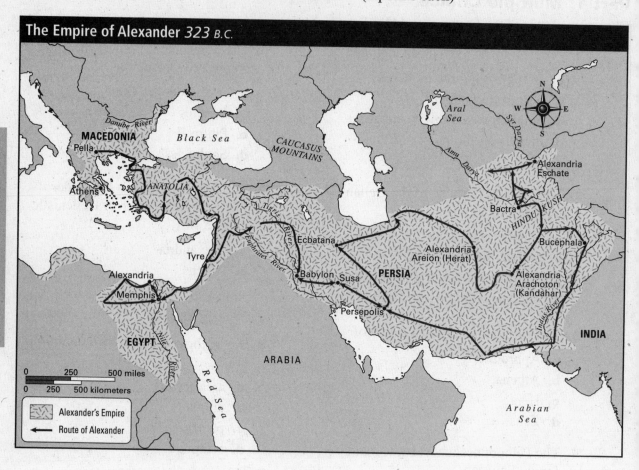

The Empire of Alexander *323* B.C.

11. What does this map show?

    a. the extent of Alexander's empire

    b. battles in which Alexander fought

    c. regions conquered by the Persians

    d. trade routes from Greece to Persia

12. Where did the route of Alexander's conquests begin?

    a. Egypt   **c.** Macedonia

    b. India   **d.** Persia

13. How many cities on this map were named after Alexander?

    a. one **b.** two **c.** three **d.** four

14. What was the largest kingdom conquered by Alexander?

    a. Egypt   **c.** Macedonia

    b. India   **d.** Persia

15. Near what waterway did Alexander's eastward march stop?

    a. Euphrates River

    b. Indus River

    c. Nile River

    d. Tigris River

Part 3: Interpreting Charts

Using the exhibit, choose the letter of the best answer. (4 points each)

SELECTED GREEK INVENTIONS			
Invention	Inventor	Date Invented	Purpose
astrolabe	Uncertain, probably Hipparchus or Apollonius of Perga	c. 200 B.C.	To determine the altitude of heavenly bodies
catapult	Dionysius the Elder	399 B.C.	To hurl spears and other objects through the air; used mainly in warfare
compound pulley	Archimedes	c. 260 B.C.	To lift heavy objects
steam engine	Heron	c. 100 B.C.	To create usable energy; considered a toy in ancient Greece

_____ 16. Who invented the catapult?

    a. Archimedes

    b. Dionysius the Elder

    c. Heron

    d. Philip II

_____ 17. The inventor of which Greek item is uncertain?

    a. astrolabe

    b. catapult

    c. compound pulley

    d. steam engine

_____ 18. Which item was invented first?

    a. astrolabe

    b. catapult

    c. compound pulley

    d. steam engine

_____ 19. Which invention was used mainly in warfare?

    a. astrolabe

    b. catapult

    c. compound pulley

    d. steam engine

_____ 20. Who invented a tool to lift heavy objects?

    a. Archimedes

    b. Dionysus the Elder

    c. Heron

    d. Hipparchus

CHAPTER 8

Part 4: Extended Response

Answer the following questions on the back of this paper or on a separate sheet of paper. (10 points each)

21. How did Athens come to dominate the Delian League?

Think About

- why the league was created
- what role Athens' navy played in the league
- how money affected power in the league

22. How did Greek art and architecture reflect Greek ideals?

Think About

- Greek concept of the ideal
- Greek ideas of order, beauty, and harmony
- Greek sculpture and architecture

CHAPTER

8

CHAPTER 8 TEST

Classical Greece

Part 1: Multiple Choice

Choose the letter of the best answer. (4 points each)

_____ **1.** The Age of _____ lasted from about 460 B.C. to 429 B.C.

    a. Alexander

    b. Pericles

    c. Sophocles

    d. Zeus

_____ **2.** Pericles expanded the role of _____ citizens in government.

    a. enslaved

    b. female

    c. poor

    d. wealthy

_____ **3.** Money from _____ was used by Pericles to rebuild Athens.

    a. the slaves

    b. poor Athenians

    c. the Delian League

    d. foreign trade partners

_____ **4.** The Peloponnesian War was caused by _____ towards Athens by other city-states.

    a. admiration

    b. pity

    c. resentment

    d. respect

_____ **5.** The _____ in Athens contributed to its defeat by Sparta.

    a. schools

    b. poor military

    c. democratic government

    d. plague

_____ **6.** Philip II was able to conquer Greek states because of his _____ tactics.

    a. economic

    b. military

    c. political

    d. social

_____ **7.** Before attacking Persia, Alexander conquered _____ .

    a. Arabia

    b. Egypt

    c. India

    d. Mesopotamia

_____ **8.** Alexandria became a center of _____ in the Hellenistic world.

    a. economics

    b. government

    c. learning

    d. military training

_____ **9.** Greek art and architecture celebrated _____ and honored the gods.

    a. beauty

    b. chaos

    c. nature

    d. politicians

_____ **10.** _____ was one of the major Greek philosophers.

    a. Aristotle

    b. Herodotus

    c. Pericles

    d. Ptolemy

Part 2: Map Skills

Using the exhibit, answer the questions. (4 points each)

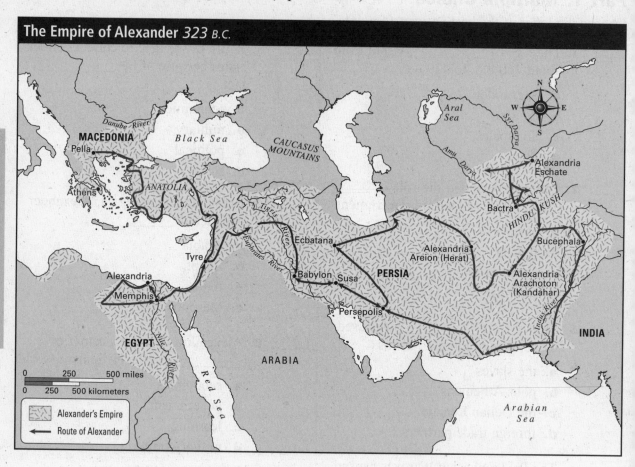

The Empire of Alexander 323 B.C.

_____ **11.** What was the easternmost city conquered by Alexander?

   a. Athens

   b. Babylon

   c. Bucephala

   d. Memphis

_____ **12.** In what city did Alexander shift from moving eastward to moving northward?

   a. Herat

   b. Pella

   c. Persepolis

   d. Susa

_____ **13.** What river formed the northern border of Macedonia?

   a. Danube River

   b. Indus River

   c. Nile River

   d. Tigris River

14. Which of the cities shown on the map were renamed for Alexander?

_____

15. What natural landform made it difficult to reach Bactra from the south?

_____

Part 3: Interpreting Charts

Using the exhibit, answer the questions. (4 points each)

SELECTED GREEK INVENTIONS			
Invention	Inventor	Date Invented	Purpose
astrolabe	Uncertain, probably Hipparchus or Apollonius of Perga	c. 200 B.C.	To determine the altitude of heavenly bodies
catapult	Dionysius the Elder	399 B.C.	To hurl spears and other objects through the air; used mainly in warfare
compound pulley	Archimedes	c. 260 B.C.	To lift heavy objects
steam engine	Heron	c. 100 B.C.	To create usable energy; considered a toy in ancient Greece

_____ **16.** Who invented the astrolabe?

    a. Archimedes

    b. Dionysius the Elder

    c. Heron

    d. uncertain

_____ **17.** Who invented a weapon used in war?

    a. Archimedes

    b. Dionysus the Elder

    c. Heron

    d. Hipparchus

_____ **18.** What invention was not put to practical use in ancient Greece?

    a. astrolabe

    b. catapult

    c. compound pulley

    d. steam engine

19. About how much time passed between the earliest and latest invention shown?

_____

20. Which invention was mostly like used by astronomers?

_____

Part 4: Extended Response

Answer the following questions on the back of this paper or on a separate sheet of paper. (10 points each)

21. How did the Peloponnesian War change Greece?

Think About

• why the war broke out
• how it affected Athens and Sparta
• how it affected the conquest by the Macedonians

22. Do you think Alexander was worthy of the title "the Great"? Explain.

Think About

• the size of his empire
• the cultural changes he brought
• the end to his empire

CHAPTER 8

CHAPTER

8

CHAPTER 8 TEST
Classical Greece

Part 1: Multiple Choice

Choose the letter of the best answer. (4 points each)

_____ 1. How did Pericles reform government in Athens?

   a. He expanded the rights of slaves.

   b. He gave more power to the poor.

   c. He gave more power to the rich.

   d. He limited public service.

_____ 2. What was an unexpected outcome of the Delian League?

   a. The power of Athens increased.

   b. The power of Athens decreased.

   c. The sea routes became less safe.

   d. Trade with other nations declined.

_____ 3. Why did Pericles rebuild Athens?

   a. A flood destroyed the city.

   b. Buildings had been neglected.

   c. He wanted the honor.

   d. Persians destroyed the city.

_____ 4. The main cause of the Peloponnesian War was resentment of what city-state?

   a. Athens   c. Persia

   b. Macedonia   d. Sparta

_____ 5. What was one result of the Peloponnesian War?

   a. Very few Greeks died.

   b. Cities and crops were destroyed.

   c. Greek city-states gained power.

   d. Greece conquered Macedonia.

_____ 6. Hellenistic scholars combined the scientific knowledge of which cultures?

   a. Germany, Egypt, India

   b. Greece, Egypt, India

   c. Greece, Egypt, Ireland

   d. Greece, India, Peru

_____ 7. Why was Alexander's empire divided after his death?

   a. He ordered that it be divided.

   b. No general could control it.

   c. It was organized into city-states.

   d. The Greeks rebelled.

_____ 8. How did Thucydides change the way history was written?

   a. He used folk tales.

   b. He used travel logs.

   c. He used Herodotus' works.

   d. He used documents and eyewitness accounts.

_____ 9. *Seven Against Thebes* is an example of what art form?

   a. comedy   c. philosophy

   b. history   d. tragedy

_____ 10. What did Aristotle have do to with Alexander the Great?

   a. Aristotle governed Alexandria.

   b. Aristotle lost a battle to Alexander.

   c. Alexander married Aristotle's daughter.

   d. Aristotle tutored Alexander.

Part 2: Map Skills

Using the exhibit, answer the questions. (4 points each)

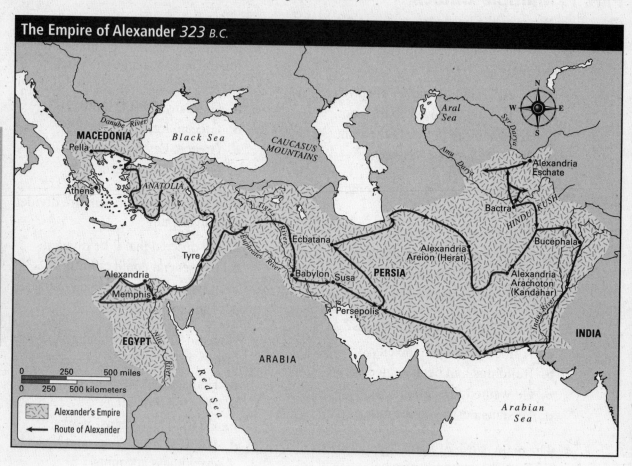

The Empire of Alexander *323* B.C.

11. In general, in what direction did Alexander expand his empire?

_____

12. Which seas bordered Alexander's empire?

_____

13. Why were some cities' names changed to Alexandria?

_____

14. Why was control of Egypt, which the Persians held, important to Alexander?

_____

15. About how far apart were Persepolis and Babylon?

_____

Part 3: Interpreting Charts

Using the exhibit, answer the questions. (4 points each)

SELECTED GREEK INVENTIONS			
Invention	Inventor	Date Invented	Purpose
astrolabe	Uncertain, probably Hipparchus or Apollonius of Perga	c. 200 B.C.	To determine the altitude of heavenly bodies
catapult	Dionysius the Elder	399 B.C.	To hurl spears and other objects through the air; used mainly in warfare
compound pulley	Archimedes	c. 260 B.C.	To lift heavy objects
steam engine	Heron	c. 100 B.C.	To create usable energy; considered a toy in ancient Greece

16. Which invention was created last?

_____

17. If you were going into war, which invention would be the most useful?

_____

18. Which invention that became very important was not put to practical use by the Greeks?

_____

19. How are the catapult and the compound pulley similar?

_____

20. What does the table say for certain about the inventor of the astrolabe?

_____

Part 4: Extended Response

Answer the following questions on the back of this paper or on a separate sheet of paper. (10 points each)

21. How might the world have been different if Alexander had lived longer?

22. How did Socrates shape the Hellenistic world?

WRITING ABOUT HISTORY
Ancient and Classical Greece

Persuasive Writing: Honoring an Ancient Leader

Purpose: To persuade a historical society to honor the leader of your choice with a statue

Audience: Members of the historical society

You read on page 394 that Pericles convinced people who saw him lose a wrestling match that he had really won. How did he do that? He used persuasion. Writing intended to convince another person to adopt your opinion or position is called persuasive writing.

Source: Bust of Pericles, Athenian statesman. Museo Pio Clementino, Vatican Museums, Vatican State. Photo © Scala/Art Resource, New York.

Organization & Focus

A historical society has raised money to erect a statue. Its goal is to honor the ancient Hebrew or ancient Greek who had the most-lasting influence on history. Your assignment is to write a 500- to 700-word letter to persuade the society to honor the leader of your choice.

Choosing a Topic Chapters 10, 11, and 12. In your notebook, write the name of each leader you find. Take notes about his or her accomplishments and lasting influence. Even if you find a leader you want to recommend, keep reviewing the chapters. To write a good persuasive letter, you will need to show why your leader is a better choice than other leaders. So you will need details about them too. When you've finished, review your notes and make your choice.

Identifying Purpose and Audience Your purpose is to use facts, examples, and reasons to convince others to adopt your opinion. Your audience is the members of a historical society. Because they are familiar with history, you won't have to provide much background information. You can focus on giving solid and convincing reasons.

Finding Supporting Evidence Gather facts, examples, and reasons to prove that your leader is the best choice. Also, anticipate the leaders others might suggest, and gather evidence against those choices.

Research & Technology

Give your readers a strong sense of your leader's personality. One way to do this is to describe actions that demonstrate the leader's best characteristics. You can find additional information about the life of your leader in the library or online. Record helpful information on a chart like the one below.

Characteristics	Actions that Demonstrate Them

Outlining and Drafting: Make an outline of the three main parts of your persuasive letter. The introduction should grab the readers' interest and state your recommendation. The body of your letter should offer facts and examples as supporting evidence for your recommendation. The body of your letter should also show why other recommendations—counterarguments—are not as good as yours. The conclusion should tie everything together and make a strong appeal.

Evaluation & Revision

Exchange first drafts with a classmate. Use the following guide to evaluate your partner's letter:

- Is the thesis statement clear?
- How strong are the main arguments and evidence?
- Were counterarguments addressed well
- Were you convinced by the letter? Why or why not?

Listen carefully to your partner's comments. Rework your letter until you are satisfied that you have addressed your partner's major concerns.

> **Self-Check**
> Does my letter have
> - ☐ an awareness of my audience and purpose?
> - ☐ an introduction that states my recommendation
> - ☐ well-organized and convincing evidence?
> - ☐ a strong conclusion with a final appeal?

Publish & Present

Make a neat final copy of your letter. Make a sketch to go along with it to show what the statue might look like. Post your letter and drawing on the bulletin board and read what others have posted there.

Answer Key

Chapter 7

Starting with a Story, *p. 1*

1. Similarities: both independent Greek city-states; both in danger of attack by the Persians. Differences: Athens placed importance on politics, education, and the arts; Sparta placed importance on military strength.
2. Students' letters should explain why Sparta should or should not help Athens. Judge letters based on content, organization, and clarity.

Section 1:
Reading Study Guide

1. traveling over land
2. uniting under a single government
3. water OR seas
4. olive oil
5. wine
6. wool
7. fine pottery
8. Mycenaean
9. alphabet
10. Anatolia
11. Greece
12. Just the lower peninsula should be labeled, not all of Greece.
13. The Ionian is to the west, the Aegean to the east of Greece.
14. They used the seas for transportation and for fishing.

Section 2:
Reading Study Guide

1. myths
2. hope
3. Poseidon
4. Athena
5. Olympic games
6. Hera
7. "bend and change" "power, honor, strength"
8. Achilles
9. He feels angry. The speaker wants Achilles to control his anger.

Section 3:
Reading Study Guide

1. a king or queen with supreme power
2. as monarchies
3. rule by the few
4. wealth or land ownership
5. citizens make political decisions
6. direct democracy
7. the laws
8. elected representatives
9. free adult males
10. leave Athens for ten years
11. serve in the army
12. serve on juries
13. To the mass of the people I gave the power they needed, / Neither degrading them, nor giving them too much rein.
14. I stood guard with a broad shield before both parties / And prevented either from triumphing unjustly.
15. There might have been a struggle for power between rich and poor Athenians. Whichever side had won would have oppressed the other.

Section 4:
Reading Study Guide

1. focused on military; government was part monarchy, part oligarchy, and part democracy; allowed women more freedom
2. had slaves; united against Persia
3. had a democracy; focused on citizenship; allowed women less freedom
4. 490 B.C.
5. Athenians and Persians
6. Athenians
7. Thermopylae
8. Spartans and Persians
9. Persians
10. 480 B.C.
11. Athenians
12. The dead or injured soldier in the center should be outlined.
13. Captions should describe the battle of Marathon, Thermopylae, or the naval battle between Athens and the Persians.

Section 1:
Reading Study Guide with Additional Support

1. a. traveling by land; b. transportation routes; c. the Mediterranean Sea and Black Sea
2. Mountains made transportation difficult; farming took place between the mountains.
3. olive oil, wine, wool, and fine pottery

4. The Greeks stopped keeping written records from 1200 to 750 B.C.

5. Greece should be labeled.

6. The Peloponnesus should be circled.

Section 2:
Reading Study Guide with Additional Support

1. a. myths; b. the Olympics; c. Poseidon

2. They had both human and divine qualities.

3. They were part of a major festival that honored Zeus.

4. the Trojan War

5. "bend and change" "power, honor, strength"

Section 3:
Reading Study Guide with Additional Support

1. a. a king or queen; b. as monarchies; c. "rule by the few." d. wealth; e. citizens make political decisions; f. direct democracy

2. The mountain ranges prevented unity and encouraged the development of city-states.

3. monarchy, aristocracy, oligarchy, rule by tyrant

4. Solon and Cleisthenes

5. To the mass of the people I gave the power they needed, / Neither degrading them, nor giving them too much rein.

Section 4:
Reading Study Guide with Additional Support

1. a. focused on military; had a government that was part monarchy, part oligarchy, and part democracy;

allowed women more freedom. b. had slaves; united against Persia. c. had a democracy; focused on citizenship; allowed women less freedom.

2. They received military training.

3. to prepare them to be good citizens

4. to stop the Persians from reaching Athens

5. Captions should describe the battle of Marathon, Thermopylae, or the naval battle between Athens and the Persians.

Building Background
Vocabulary, *p. 35*

1. e

2. d

3. b

4. g

5. a

6. c

7. h

8. f

9. rough , smooth

10. lively , dull

11. slowly , rapid

12. smart , slow-witted

Vocabulary
Practice, *p. 36*

1. Zeus

2. helot

3. citizen

4. Phoenician

5. tyrant

6. Sparta

7. Peloponnesus

8. Mount Olympus

9. Athens

10. Monarchy

11. oligarchy

12. Olympics

13. alphabet

14. barracks

15. polis

Skillbuilder
Practice, *p. 37*

1. The ancient Greeks used several different types of boats.

2. They used square sails on their fishing boats and trading boats. Their fighting ships were built for speed and mobility.

3. Triremes were too low to go on ocean voyages, and it would be difficult or impossible for men to row over such long distances.

History Makers, *p. 39*

1. The *Iliad* takes place during the Trojan War, a struggle between the Greeks and Trojans.

2. It tells about the adventures of Odysseus as he returns home from the Trojan War.

3. A long poem about heroes and their actions.

4. Epic poems tell of heroic actions. They use repetition and stock phrases. They were part of an oral tradition.

5. Homer's poems were part of the Greek heritage. They helped students think about why people act the way they do.

6. the discovery of the site of the historical Troy by Heinrich Schliemann

Connect Geography & History, *p. 41*

1. the coast or the sea
2. Aegean Sea
3. Students should link Mycenae to each of the other cities shown on the map. The lines will radiate outward from Mycenae.
4. It was in a central location.
5. Mycenaean culture spread by sea travel, through migration or trade.

6. The map should show Knossos and Phaistos. It might also show Khana, Mallia, or Kato Zakro.

Outline Map Activity, *p. 43*

1. Marathon
2. about 600 miles
3. Sardis
4. 1
5. about 25 miles
6. because of all the islands and the long coastlines of their territories
7. 11 years
8. The battles were fought on their territory, so they were familiar with the terrain.
9. 5

Primary and Secondary Sources, *p. 45*

1. by their foolishness, unjust minds, outrageous behaviors and corruption
2. good government
3. Slavery, because it creates conflict and leads to war.
4. He is trying to get Athenians to correct their

behaviors and to embrace good government.

Literature, *p. 46*

1. because he blinded his son; by preventing Odysseus from getting home
2. that the gods were directly involved in the lives of people
3. She will give him courage to speak.

Reader's Theater, *p. 47*

1. Possible answers: She can do what men can do; she does not need support or protection; she is not in love with any man; she was abandoned by her father and might feel that no man deserves her trust.
2. Evaluate student paragraphs on how well they describe the race and on grammar, spelling, and punctuation.

Section 1 Quiz, *p. 65*

1. d
2. c
3. b
4. b
5. a
6. a
7. b
8. d
9. a
10. c

Section 2 Quiz, *p. 66*

1. d
2. c
3. d
4. c
5. b

6. a
7. d
8. a
9. c
10. b

Section 3 Quiz, *p. 67*

1. d
2. a
3. d
4. d
5. c
6. a
7. b
8. a
9. d
10. b

Section 4 Quiz, *p. 68*

1. a
2. c
3. b
4. c
5. b
6. b
7. a
8. d
9. d
10. d

Section 1 Reteaching Activity

1. i
2. h
3. f
4. a
5. g
6. e
7. d
8. j
9. b
10. c

Section 2 Reteaching Activity

1. Mount Olympus

2. Athena
3. myth
4. fire
5. Zeus
6. epics
7. Trojan War
8. fable

Section 3
Reteaching Activity

1. A city-state is a state made of a city and its surrounding lands.
2. Athens and Sparta
3. the agora, an open space where people gathered for business and public gatherings
4. In Greek cities, an acropolis was a fortified hilltop used for military purposes or to build temples and palaces.
5. monarchy, a government in which a king or queen rules
6. An oligarchy is rule by a small group because of its wealth or land ownership.
7. A tyrant was someone who took power in an illegal way and who acted like a king without being of royal birth.
8. Today, citizen refers to a person who is loyal to a government and who is entitled to protection by that government.
9. a democracy
10. Athens' democracy was limited because only adult free males were citizens who could take part in government.

Section 4
Reteaching Activity

1. c

2. a
3. b
4. d

5. Sparta's government was a mixture of democracy, oligarchy, and monarchy. Two kings ruled Sparta, and five elected supervisors ran its government. The Council of Elders proposed laws, and the Assembly, made up of all Spartan citizens, voted on the laws and elected officials.
6. Spartan society expected its women to be tough. They were to encourage their sons to fight. Women received athletic training and had more freedom. They were allowed to own property.
7. In Athens, boys of wealthy families learned logic, public speaking, reading, writing, poetry, arithmetic, music, and athletics.

Chapter Test A, *p. 73*

1. c
2. d
3. b
4. c
5. b
6. a
7. a
8. c
9. a
10. b

11. d
12. a
13. c
14. a
15. c

16. a
17. d
18. b
19. c
20. b
21. defeat the wealthy
22. an embroidered robe
23. liberty
24. having a discussion
25. Plato says that democracy allows each person to live "his own life as he pleases." Plato also says that a democracy will include a wide variety of people. Aristotle emphasizes that democracy is based on liberty and that every citizen is equal.

Chapter Test B, *p. 79*

1. c
2. b
3. c
4. c
5. d
6. b
7. c
8. c
9. a
10. b

11. c
12. a
13. a

14. Hemeroscopium
15. 200 miles

16. d
17. b
18. c
19. a
20. c
21. The poor must defeat the wealthy.

22. It has the greatest variety of people.
23. the poor
24. The image suggests that Plato and Aristotle had different ideas.
25. Both emphasized that democracy brings freedom and equality. But Plato placed greater emphasis on how democracy creates diversity. Aristotle emphasized liberty and how a democratic society gives people greater freedom to do what they want.

Chapter Test C, *p. 85*

1. a
2. a
3. c
4. d
5. c
6. b
7. a
8. a
9. d
10. c

11. It implies that the Greeks were skilled sailors.
12. Black Sea
13. More Greeks probably lived on Cyprus, which was a Greek homeland.
14. about 350 miles
15. Al Mina

16. monarchy
17. because citizenship was limited to free adult males
18. because they controlled the military
19. Athens 500 b.c.)
20. Power was redistributed from the rich and the nobles to the poor and middle class.
21. People will have the freedom to pursue their own interests, and this will lead to a greater diversity of human natures and activities.
22. The poor must give an equal share of freedom and power to the conquered.
23. In ancient Greek democracy, all citizens participated in government. Since leaders were elected at random, people had the opportunity to serve both as rulers and as citizens.
24. The image suggests that Plato taught Aristotle through books and discussion.
25. Plato's comparison of democracy to a colorful robe implies that democracy looks appealing but may not work as well as it looks. Aristotle seems to criticize majority rule when he says, "whatever the majority approve must be the end and the just."

Chapter 8

Starting with a Story, *p. 91*

1. Possible answer: Pericles shows respect and concern for the rights of all citizens. He will need to be persuasive and persistent to get the policy enacted.
2. Students' papers should clearly and precisely state their positions. They should provide points of support as well as address objections.

Section 1:
Reading Study Guide

1. to strengthen Athens' democracy by spreading power more equally among Athenians
2. to expand Athens' power abroad
3. to beautify the city, which had been damaged during the Persian Wars
4. Some city-states feared Athens; other city-states resented Athens' use of funds from the Delian League.
5. Sparta declares war on Athens in 431 B.C.; people take refuge inside the walls of Athens; plague kills about one-third of Athenians, including Pericles; truce signed in 421 B.C.; Athens attacks Sicily in 415 B.C.; Sparta attacks Athens in 411 B.C.; Athens surrenders in 404 B.C.
6. cities and crops destroyed, thousands of Greeks died, city-states lose economic and military power

7. The Parthenon is at the top of the picture in the center.
8. Captions should indicate that the Acropolis is pictured.

Section 2:
Reading Study Guide

1. gave Macedonian forces an advantage
2. made other Greek city-states too fearful to rebel
3. Alexander controlled the Persian Empire
4. Greek styles and customs with Persian, Egyptian, and Indian styles and customs
5. new discoveries in science and medicine
6. a research center for the arts and sciences
7. Egypt, Persia, and India should be labeled.
8. the Persian Gulf
9. Mediterranean, Black, Caspian, Arabian

Section 3:
Reading Study Guide

1. tragedy and comedy
2. order, beauty, and harmony
3. Athens
4. philosophy
5. the earth
6. geometry
7. Aeschylus, Aristophanes
8. Phidias
9. Herodotus and Thucydides
10. Socrates, Plato, Aristotle
11. Eratosthenes, Aristarchus, Ptolemy
12. Euclid, Archimedes, Hypatia
13. The two birds in the girl's hands should be circled.
14. This sculpture shows the Greek sense of order,

balance, and proportion. It is also an example of how Greek artists portrayed ideal forms.

Section 1:
Reading Study Guide with Additional Support

1. a. strengthen Athens' democracy
   b. expand Athens' power abroad
   c. beautify the city
2. by spreading power more evenly and paying elected officials
3. It took over control of the Delian League.
4. He took funds from the Delian League.
5. the plague and the destruction of the Athenian navy
6. The Parthenon is at the top of the picture in the center.
7. Captions should indicate that the Acropolis is pictured.

Section 2:
Reading Study Guide with Additional Support

1. a. gave Macedonian forces an advantage; b. made other Greek city-states too fearful to rebel; c. ended the Persian Empire and spread Greek culture
2. They were weak and disorganized after the Peloponnesian War.
3. His armies needed a break after 11 years of battles.
4. The conquests of Alexander led to a blending of Greek, Persian, Egyptian, and Indian cultures.
5. Egypt, Persia, and India should be labeled.

Section 3: Reading Study Guide with Additional Support

1. a. tragedy and comedy; b. order, beauty, and harmony; c. Athens; d. philosophy; e. the earth; f. geometry
2. ideal forms; order, beauty, harmony; graceful proportions
3. It developed democracy.
4. Alexandria
5. This sculpture shows the Greek sense of order, balance, and proportion.

Building Background Vocabulary, *p. 117*

1. league
2. glorify
3. strategy
4. hostage
5. tutored
6. sponsor
7. troupe
8. proportions
9. compound

Vocabulary Practice, *p. 118*

1. See column 8.
2. See column 7.
3. See column 9.
4. See row 3.
5. See column 1.
6. See column 4.
7. See column 5.

8. Pericles
9. Alexander
10. Socrates, Plato, Aristotle
11. Direct democracy
12. Peloponnesian
13. Alexandria

Skillbuilder Practice, *p. 119*

1. Source 5

2. Sources 2, 3, and 5
3. Sources 1 and 4, because they are written by authors whose knowledge is questionable.
4. Is he an expert in this field?

History Makers, *p. 121*

1. Plato
2. the Lyceum; in Athens
3. observation
4. Possible answers: explanation of earth science, because he had no modern scientific equipment; writing at least 150 books, which shows his wide range of knowledge; classification of animals, which is a huge project for one person; use of observation to learn and teach, because this was a new and effective method
5. Answers will vary, but students should select one of the quotations in the text and clearly explain what it means.
6. His works were used to teach grammar, logic, and rhetoric. His classification system of animals remained basically unchanged until the 1800s. Students of philosophy still study his ideas.

Connect Geography & History, *p. 123*

1. Panthenaic Way
2. Statue of Athena Promachos
3. about 40 by 85 yards (35 by 75 meters)
4. Erectheum

5. Students should circle the temple directly south of the Propyla.

6. from left to right: Propyla, Chalcothece, Parthenon

Outline Map Activity, *p. 125*

1. Athens and Sparta
2. Athens
3. Spartalos (429 b.c.)
4. Athens won three (Cynossema, Cyzicus, and Sphacteria) and Sparta won three (Amphipolis, Notium, and Spartalos).
5. They lost a battle so close to their city-state.
6. about 260 miles
7. Amphipolis
8. 27 years
9. The war probably would not have lasted so long, because it would not take as long to transport the troops and equipment to battle sites.
10. Macedonia

Primary and Secondary Sources, *p. 129*

1. They will know they were defeated by a superior force.
2. They have forced all enemies to respect them for their valor and have left behind monuments and memorials to friendship.
3. For in the hour of trial Athens alone among her contemporaries is superior to the report of her.
4. Yes, its point is to show that those who died in war did not die in vain. Presidents

often say that in times of war.

Literature, *p. 130*

1. They had run him off the road.
2. No one should speak to him or give him shelter; everyone should avoid him.
3. Possible answer: Oedipus feels horrible about having killed his father.
4. It is a serious drama that deals with the downfall of an important character.

Section 1 Quiz, *p. 143*

1. c
2. a
3. b
4. a
5. d
6. a
7. d
8. c
9. d
10. c

Section 2 Quiz, *p. 144*

1. b
2. c
3. d
4. c
5. d
6. a
7. b
8. d
9. b
10. b

Section 3 Quiz, *p. 145*

1. b
2. d
3. a
4. c
5. b
6. a
7. d

8. a
9. b
10. a

Section 1
Reteaching Activity

1. Pericles
2. direct democracy
3. Delian League
4. Acropolis
5. Peloponnesian War
6. navy
7. plague
8. truce
9. Athens, Sparta

Section 2
Reteaching Activity

1. He developed a professional army and used advanced weapons and tactics.
2. First, he suppressed a rebellion in Thebes. Next, he defeated the Persians in Anatolia. Then he took over Egypt. Finally, he crossed Mesopotamia and attacked the capital of Persia, Persepolis.
3. Alexander encouraged his followers to adopt the styles and customs of the conquered lands. His wide empire led to a blending of Greek, Persian, Egyptian, and Indian cultures.

4. a
5. b
6. c
7. e
8. d

Section 3
Reteaching Activity

1. invented drama; built the first theaters in the western world; developed the

tragedy and the comedy; pursued the portrayal of the ideal in sculpture
2. developed distinct elements including the column and the colonnade
3. left behind the idea of democracy; Greek citizens practiced direct democracy.
4. Eratosthenes discovered how to estimate the circumference of the Earth; Aristarchus estimated the size of the sun.
5. Euclid's work provided the basis for geometry.

6. b
7. c
8. d
9. e
10. a

Chapter Test A, *p. 149*

1. b
2. b
3. b
4. c
5. b
6. c
7. a
8. b
9. d
10. c

11. a
12. c
13. d
14. d
15. b

16. b
17. a
18. b
19. b
20. a

21. The city-states formed the Delian League for the purpose of mutual protection. Since Athens had the strongest navy, it took control of the league. It then moved the league's treasury to Athens. Pericles used money from the treasury to rebuild Athens. Athens began to treat the other city-states like conquered people.

22. Greek artists aimed to capture the ideal in their work. They worked to create a sense of order, proportion, beauty, and harmony in both their art and architecture. That meant showing objects, buildings, and people in as perfect a form as possible.

Chapter Test B, *p. 153*

1. b
2. c
3. c
4. c
5. d
6. b
7. b
8. c
9. a
10. a

11. c
12. c
13. a

14. Alexandria, Egypt; Alexandria Areion; Alexandria Arachoton; Alexandria Eschate
15. the Hindu Kush mountains

16. d

17. b
18. d

19. about 300 years
20. astrolabe

21. Before the war, Athens was the strongest city-state in Greece. Athens's control of the Delian League and use of league money for its own purposes angered many other city-states. Finally, the other city-states, led by Sparta, rebelled against Athens. Pericles' policy of moving the population into Athens and letting Sparta destroy the countryside led to disaster. When a plague hit Athens, one-third of the population died, including Pericles. By the time Athens surrendered to Sparta, it had lost most of its power. The other Greek city-states were also weakened by years of war. This made it easier for the Macedonians to conquer Greece.

22. Possible answer #1: Yes, Alexander does deserve the title. His empire was enormous by any standard and was created in only 11 years. The cultural changes lasted long after he died and continued to influence the world for a long time. Possible answer #2: No, Alexander does not deserve the title. He was skilled at killing and conquering, but that does not make a man great. His empire fell apart almost as soon as he died because it was only held together by fear. Hellenistic culture would have happened without Alexander because trade routes would have led to a similar blending of cultures and ideas.

Chapter Test C, *p. 157*

1. b
2. a
3. d
4. a
5. b
6. b
7. b
8. d
9. d
10. d

11. from west to east
12. Mediterranean, Black, Caspian, Arabian (Red Sea also acceptable)
13. to honor the conqueror
14. Alexander needed to gain control of Egypt before advancing into Persia to avoid an attack from Persians in Egypt.
15. a little more than 500 miles (800 kilometers)

16. the steam engine
17. the catapult
18. steam engine
19. Both are used to handle heavy objects.
20. The inventor was Greek, or the inventor lived around 200 b.c.

21. Answers will vary but should note that Alexander died before he had time to unify his empire. His empire might have lasted

longer if he had lived. Also, Alexander did not expand his empire further east than the Indus River. Had he lived, he might have later moved further east, and perhaps more of Asia would have adopted aspects of Hellenistic culture.

22. Socrates was one of Greece's most important philosophers. He taught his students to examine their beliefs and challenged them with questions. After Socrates died, his students continued to develop his ideas and methods. Plato, one of Socrates' best students, opened the Academy. Both Plato and his student Aristotle developed important and influential ideas about government. Many of the ideas of Hellenistic philosophy were inspired by Socrates and his students.